LASER ART
& OPTICAL TRANSFORMS

Leo Beiser. *Clouds of Light.* Perspective rendering of the 3-dimensional field intensity of a converging spherical wave diffracted at a circular aperture. (Courtesy Leo Beiser Inc.; *Applied Optics*, vol. 4, page 869. May, 1966.)

LASER ART
&
OPTICAL TRANSFORMS

by T. KALLARD

With a Foreword by ROSEMARY H. JACKSON
Director, *Museum of Holography*

Associate Editor
MILTON WALLER

optosonic press

LASER ART & OPTICAL TRANSFORMS by Thomas Kallard

First published in the United States of America in 1979 by:

OPTOSONIC PRESS
Scientific, Technical and Business Books
Box 883, Ansonia Post Office
New York, N.Y. 10023 (USA)

Front cover: Optical transform by T. Kallard
Back cover: Photo by T. Kallard; live laser image from *LASERIUM, the
Original Cosmic Laser Concert* (Produced by Laser Images, Inc.)
Cover design: Alan Solomon

Uncredited illustrations are by the author

First Printing

Library of Congress Catalog Card Number: 78-70638
International Standard Book Number: 0-87739-009-6

Manufactured in the United States of America

FOREWORD

A Little Light Writing

If the laser is the pencil of the 20th Century, then this is its sketchbook —
certainly not the 'complete works,' as that is presumably as infinite as the
collective human imagination that could fill it, but an index of known
possibilities. More literally, it is an anthology of creative visual imagery made
with and made *of* laser light, a collection of optical sketches in which the
laser is used as both subject and medium.

Laser art is usually classified as 'technological art,' meaning that it uses some
highly advanced and improved technical means to deliver (or be) its message.
While this is certainly true, it also tends to exclude laser art from the
mainstream of more traditional, manually produced art (such as painting or
sculpture) intimating that the latter is more creative because it is a product of
direct human skill, and the former more automatic (read "less creative")
because it relies on optical or electronic systems for image generation. (People
who have trouble realizing machines are simply an organic extension of their
own skills refer to the end result as artifice, rather than art.) Apparently one is
not supposed to advance the tools of one's art with the changing technology
of the times, and above all, one is not supposed to confuse the issue by using a
machine that was directed by a human hand. In an age where almost nothing
is made by hand (and is not necessarily the worse for wear) why do we still
insist that artists perform such ancient rites? After all, laser technology is to
the 20th Century what printing technology was to the 15th. Both were
introduced as radically innovative communications media, using the most
highly advanced technology of the times. And both were quickly taken up by
the artists of the period as media capable of carrying the creative message a
little further than before. In short, it is no more unusual for a modern artist
to be working with a laser than it was for Albrecht Dürer to use the printing
press.

All art is technological in that it is made by those who push constantly at the
parameters of the known and the comfortable, and use the tools found at these
outer edges to special purpose. In fact, the term "technological art" is an

anachronism. All art involves the advanced craft and process of some technology. Laser light is simply another tool for the art process like egg tempera, stained glass, and charred sticks. Used with imagination and skill (the Greek root *technē* means art, craft, skill) it becomes special enough to be art.

The works illustrated in this book include art made with laser light (holography) and art made of laser light (optical transforms, 'lasergrams', and light shows). It is important to remember that the illustrations are artifacts of the original work, photo reproductions on paper of the original light imagery in space. This transition has, of necessity, removed the most dramatic element of the art — that very special grainy brilliance of the laser light itself. If one could only reproduce this in a book! However, in the case of the optical transforms and lasergrams, the graphic conversion provides as interesting a visual in its own right as the original image. (I prefer the photos of the lasergrams over the negative images of these patterns which have been directly projected onto film because the former reproduce more of the natural dynamism of light. The latter, however, have been made by a more interesting creative process.) It is not surprising that the visual integrity of these images remains after printing, as many of them were flat to begin with, and were produced as shadows of a sort at that. Thus, they adapted well to the black and white format of the printed page. In fact, they work as well graphically as they do in a live laser light show, despite the slightly different gestalt. Certainly the graphic reproduction and the original live image are equally as creative and intentional art works. This is one of the marvelous eccentricities of the medium: it can be both image and process, either medium or message.

The holograms, whose reconstructed images have been reproduced through photography for this book, are inevitably flat testimonials of their real selves. Yet, even these printed images, these monocular renditions of holographic space and time, hint broadly at the richness of the art, and show plainly the inherent creative capabilities — and surprising flexibility — of the medium. (Just as lasergrams, light shows and optical transforms can be live or recorded, so can holograms be 'real time' or reconstructed images.)

While most forms of laser art correspond well to pre-existing art aesthetics, holography is a challenge to our conceptions of balance and form, and the manner in which art is "read" (exactly like books, in the West at least, from top to bottom, from left to right). Holography presents us with a volume, not a flat plane, and with imagery that exists at different levels of space within this volume, unlike the flat surface of a painting or movie screen. We have to learn to adjust our thinking, and more importantly our seeing, to accept an art form that presents a multiplicity of images, that makes us the scanner, that presents both the whole and the sum of its parts. This challenge presents us with the promise of tremendous growth in our visual literacy if we can learn to perceive without immediately trying to find a compartment for our observations.

Western visual literacy evolved over thousands of years. We cannot hope to map this new terrain of holography, or the larger area of the laser arts, immediately. And we cannot hope to learn from it if we approach it with a judgmental frame of mind. (Is it really art? — Is it good?) While the laser arts provide us with a novel medium, and a more complex message, they do not require a new aesthetics, nor do they demand special tools for appreciation and understanding. Art is art, whether it is mud on a cave wall, or ink on paper. It requires only the 'tools' we were born with; our eyes, our minds and our feelings — ours, not somebody else's. Art is what you make of it, what you bring to it and what you take from it, whether it is high tech or low tech.

We can learn from art if we approach it like a friend, not dwelling on whether it is good or bad, a success or failure, but on what can be discovered, what can be taught and learned, given and received through association with it. Art makes a good friend. If you are looking for new ones, this "sketchbook" is a good place to start.

ROSEMARY H. JACKSON
Director,
Museum of Holography

New York City
January, 1979

ACKNOWLEDGMENTS

I am greatly indebted to various individuals and organizations for their generous help which made this publication possible:

For their continued interest, encouragement and assistance, I owe special thanks to Robert D. Anwyl, Eastman Kodak Company, and C. Harry Knowles, Metrologic Instruments, Inc.

To Posy Jackson for her significant Foreword, and the staff of the Museum of Holography for their interest and support.

To Milton D. Waller, my editor, for his tireless efforts and valuable suggestions, and to Robert Hupka for his much appreciated help with the pictorial material.

For permission to include their material, I would like to thank:

Leo Beiser, Leo Beiser Inc., Flushing, New York
Louis M. Brill, Wavefronts, San Francisco, California
Linda Cecere, Multiplex Company, San Francisco, California
Leon Goldman, M.D., University of Cincinnati, Cincinnati, Ohio
Walter Gundy and Jennifer Morris, Entertainment Ion, Cambridge, Mass.
Jeffrey C. Hecht, "Laser Focus," Newton, Massachusetts
R.B. Heckler, "Lighting Dimensions," Denver, Colorado
Joyce Labossiere, Laser Images, Inc., Van Nuys, California
Gene E. Maddux, Wright-Patterson AFB, Ohio
David J. Monnier, Detroit Diesel Allison, Div. of GM, Indianapolis, Ind.
Kalina Nicholson, University of Hawaii, Honolulu, Hawaii
Brian B. O'Brien, Professional Engineer, Newton, Massachusetts
Ralph Page, Apollo Lasers, Los Angeles, California
Hart Perry, Jr., The Holographic Film Co., New York, N.Y.
N.J. Phillips, University of Technology, Loughborough, Leics, U.K.
Bruce Rogers and Gary Levenberg, Soleil Co., Cranbury, New Jersey
Gerd Stern, Intermedia Systems Corp., Cambridge, Massachusetts
Karl A. Stetson, United Technologies, East Hartford, Connecticut
Ralph F. Wuerker, TRW Systems Group, Redondo Beach, California
F.T.S. Yu, Wayne State University, Detroit, Michigan

Contributing in a hundred ways were a host of individuals — laserists, holographers, photographers, and Multiprint, Inc., our printers — to whom I should like to acknowledge my indebtedness.

CONTENTS

FOREWORD: "A Little Light Writing"
by Rosemary H. Jackson v

AN HISTORICAL PERSPECTIVE 1

LASERS AND LASER LIGHT 9
    Laser Safety

LASER LIGHT GENERATED IMAGES 14
    Laser Light Environment
    Writing with Lasers
    Spirograms
    Visual Display of Sound
    Light Caustics

LASER THEATRE 37
    Lovelight
    Laserium
    Soleil

OPTICAL TRANSFORMS 53
    Introduction
    The Optical Setup
    Diffraction Apertures
    Photographing the Optical Transforms
    Properties of Optical Transforms
    The Plates

HOLOGRAPHY 119
    Transmission Holograms
    White Light Reflection Holograms
    Phase Holograms
    Pulsed Laser Holograms
    Rainbow Holograms
    White Light Integral Holograms
    Holography in Science and Industry

BIBLIOGRAPHY 168

Scientists change the world without knowing it.

— *Lord Balfour*

Technology doesn't mean. It is means.

— *Robert Rauschenberg*

There is poetry everywhere in the world and in everything and it is clearly present in the world that scientists have at their braintips. There remains only the task of expressing it, of casting it into the wind that it may be carried to all man.

— *Isaac Asimov*

AN HISTORICAL PERSPECTIVE

Laser imagery as an art medium uses modern optics and electronic technology, along with traditional equipment to produce its works of art. The artist working with a laser can draw, paint and inter-weave sound with motion in black-and-white and color. Today the tools are available. Two and three-dimensional abstract forms as well as representational images are created by laser modulators, synthesizers and holography.

Laser technology was developed in the 1960's and 70's. When invented, lasers immediately fired the artistic imagination. Coherent light with its high intensity, spectral purity and pencil-like form was a new medium that begged for exploration. Modern artists began to team up with scientists and engineers in the belief that the creators of our time should work with up-to-date means. They felt the development of new technical tools would result in new fields of creativity. Many artist/scientists and scientist/artists came to work with lasers as an outgrowth of their work in other media. The work done by many individuals during the past fifteen years represents an extension of the traditional idea of art, and also of media. During the past few years the opportunities for laser artists to exhibit works at museums, galleries and planetariums has grown considerably.

Going back in time to 1925, Lászlo Moholy-Nagy, a Hungarian artist, predicted that light would bring forth an entirely new kind of art. He wrote: "It is probable that future development will attach the greatest importance to kinetic, projected composition, probably even with interpenetrating beams and masses of light floating freely in the room without a direct plane of projection; the instruments will continually be improved so that it will be able to embrace far larger fields of tension than the most highly developed static picture." Among the major artists of the 1920's and 30's only Moholy-Nagy worked with both light and movement. He traveled from Europe to the U.S. and in Chicago founded the Institute of Design where until his death in 1946, he was Director. Moholy-Nagy's principal theoretical work, "Vision in Motion" was published posthumously in 1947.

Fifty years ago Moholy-Nagy gave up painting and called for 'drawing with light' and 'light in place of pigment'. He spoke about the one-ness of art, science and technology. He said: "People believe that they should demand hand execution as an inseparable part of the genesis of a work of art. In fact, in comparison with the inventive mental process of the genesis of the work, the question of its execution is important only so far as it must be mastered to the limits. The manner, however, — whether personal or by assignment of labor, whether manual or mechanical — is irrelevant."

In 1936 Alexander Korda commissioned Moholy-Nagy to design the special effects for the film, "The Shape of Things to Come," based on the novel by H. G. Wells. Moholy-Nagy's light modulators represented the beginnings of a kinetic light art which flourishes in today's laser age.

'Op Art' is defined as a visual fine art (painting or sculpture) that evokes strong visual responses by utilizing various optical effects ('Op Art' meaning 'optical art'). Moholy-Nagy did the spadework for this school in 1942. The first Op Art exhibition was organized by his collaborator György Kepes.

It was Moholy-Nagy who invited his countryman Kepes to come to the United States to teach at the Institute in Chicago. Based on his teaching experiences there, Kepes published, "The Language of Vision," in 1945. He organized an exhibition at Harvard's Carpenter Center for the Visual Arts on the concept of "Light as a Creative Medium." In 1946 Kepes began to teach at the Massachusetts Institute of Technology and founded what later became MIT's Center for Advanced Visual Studies.

We come now to Nicolas Schöffer who lived in Paris. He began, in the 1950's to construct what he named "Luminodynamic Spectacles." They were seen in the parks and city's spaces. His "Cybernetic Tower," built in 1961 in Liège, Belgium, radiated music and light in motion.

Otto Piene and Heinz Mack of Düsseldorf formed ZERO in 1957, a group to explore new technology as new means in art. Mack exploited reflective metal surfaces and Piene used pre-cut stencils to modulate light and project his 'light paintings' on the wall, ceiling and floor. During the 1960's and early 1970's, Piene used the sky as a space or stage for 'sky events'.

Another group, GRAV, was founded in Paris in 1960 by Julio Le Parc. Gruppo T followed in Milan, Gruppo N in Padua, Equippo 57 in Spain and other groups in Holland and Germany. All explored the potential use of movement and light.

During the 1950's John Healy created 'light boxes' which projected moving shapes onto walls and screens and Frank Malina created his "Lumidyne" constructions. Malina's work was presented in the Kunst Licht Kunst exhibition in Eindhoven, Holland, in 1966. Malina founded the journal "Leonardo" a forum for artists and scientists to describe their research on new materials and techniques and to express their thoughts as to what their work meant.

The pioneer American kinetic-light art group, USCO, was formed in 1962. Gerd Stern was a founding member and spokesman for the group. It consisted of artists, engineers, poets and filmmakers who created audio-visual performances and set up a permanent light display in an abandoned Garnersville, New York, church.

The laser was invented in 1960 and within a few years Co-Op-Art, as Leo Beiser calls it ('Co-Op' for 'coherent-optical'), was born. Two years later, in Sweden Carl Frederik Reuterswärd began his exploratory work with lasers. Later, in 1968, he used laser light in a performance of "Faust" in Stockholm. Joel Stein designed installations for projecting laser images on a stage for a ballet produced by Michel Descombey at the Opera Comique in Paris. During the late 1960's Robert Whitman and James Turrell used laser light in Museum projections. Rockne Krebs, Mike Campbell and Baron Kody constructed 'environmental rooms' for "Laser Light: A New Visual Art," an exhibition organized by Dr. Leon Goldman at the Cincinnati Art Museum in December, 1969. These 'rooms' were filled with mirrors and some smoke to make the criss-crossing laser beam visible. Rockne Krebs, for example, used six helium-neon lasers and four co-planar mirrors. The mirrors were slightly bent, giving the reflected images within the 'room' a curved effect and the impression of a complicated network of brilliant red light. In 1971, with the help of argon and helium-neon lasers and mirrors, Rockne Krebs created "Day Passage." This multi-colored, three-dimensional light structure was made for "Art and Technology" at the Los Angeles County Museum of Art. Also in 1971, Willard Van De Bogart created laser images in concert with the Los Angeles Philharmonic Orchestra. The images were projected onto a 40' x 40' screen through a complex of optical glass, fiber optics; rippled plastics and mirrors.

In the early 1970's Elsa Garmire, a laser physicist at the California Institute of Technology, did pioneering work in the development of laser art. She experimented with the ability of various materials, placed in black boxes, to alter laser light by reflection and refraction. She passed a laser beam through such on optical box and projected it onto a wall, screen, or photographic film. In other instances the light was aimed at printing paper, to record negative black-and-white 'lasergrams'. Garmire's team and Ivan Dryer's company, Laser Images, Inc., made abstract films recording the ballet of forms set to music. Some of her laser photographs were exhibited at the Photosphere Gallery in Los Angeles.

In 1968 Lloyd G. Cross invented Sonovision, which produced a visual display of sound by projecting a modulated laser beam on an opaque surface or translucent screen. Music, a complex of many frequencies at any given instant, was represented as a mixture of pure tone patterns. The petal-type and Lissajous patterns were not only in correspondence to the music but also repeatable each time a particular passage was played. This device, and similar ones, later became an important part of the instruments used to make laser projections as background for poetry readings, mime, ballet and stage productions.

The term 'light show' is commonly used to describe projected kinetic art. During the 1970's a new technique evolved: scanning projection, or X-Y scanning. With X-Y, it is possible to project preconceived nonrepresentational forms, line-form drawings and illusions of three-dimensional surfaces. These projections can be aimed at walls, clouds, balloons or mountains. They may be used safely indoors when aimed at a surface such as a planetarium dome, — an entire section of this book is given over to this technology. Details of productions, such as "Lovelight" (by Intermedia Systems Corp.); "Laserium" and "Laserock" (by Laser Images, Inc.); "Laser Fantasia" and "Laser Spectacle" (by Soleil Co.) are cited and described. All over the world laser light shows are becoming more and more numerous and the interested reader should seek out the opportunity to see as many as possible.

In England, John Wolff has been involved with large scale laser displays for many years. He is a leading exponent of laser light shows and it was through the work of Wolff that "The Who," a pop group, began using laser light effects during their performances. The group's concerts are punctuated with a few 90-second bursts from their eleven lasers. During the summer of 1976 Wolff and Paul McCartney put on a laser show for the "Venice in Peril" fund, — an event organized by UNESCO. Wolff is a member of HOLOCO, a group established at Shepperton Studio Centre for the purpose of developing and producing optical effects. The other participants of the HOLOCO group are Nick Phillips, a Senior Lecturer at Loughborough University, where HOLOCO's research into holography is done, and Anton Furst, who has been involved in design, special effects and holography since 1967.

In 1975 the Massachusetts Institute of Technology hosted a conference on the use of new technologies by the arts. In 1976 the American Association of the Advancement of Science held a symposium called "Art, Science, and Technology in Shaping the Environment of the Future."

Artist Reginald Pollack produced a light show in 1977 at Pennsylvania State University. He used eight helium-neon lasers to project abstract images on a screen during the school's annual arts festival. Computer-generated and laser images were made to interact to the music of Bach and Stravinsky. For the past several years Professor Rustum Roy, also of Penn State, has been collaborating with artists in a program to educate faculty and students in the pioneering work being done with lasers. The University already has a small museum of commissioned art works, as well as an annual science in art competition.

The summer of 1978 saw nightly laser events being held in Washington, D.C. "Icarus," a sky opera, sponsored by the Smithsonian Institution and the Massachusetts Institute of Technology, was created by composer Paul Earls and artist Otto Piene of MIT's Center for Advanced Visual Studies. The laser imagery for Icarus was projected on steam screens which rose from "Centerbeam," a huge, 140-foot sculpture array which displayed MIT artworks. The argon-krypton laser beam was microprocessor manipulated to create images such as flying birds, minotaurs and a poem, which was written in laser light.

Thirty-six thousand watts of power were fed into a water-cooled argon laser to produce the sky display at "photokina '78" held in September of that year in Cologne, Germany. The blue-green laser beam appeared over the city and across the sky and connected the municipal art museum on the West bank of the Rhine with the tower of the fair complex on the East. Laser artist Horst Baumann set up an array of mirrors in the tower to deflect the principal beam at the Gothic cathedral as well as other points of interest in the area.

The "Artfest '78," sponsored by the Knoxville Arts Council, took place in October, 1978. Festivities included a laser light show, produced by Laser Displays, Inc. of Boston. Imagery was also produced by a Moog synthesizer connected to a laser modulator constructed by a local highschool student. The lasers illuminated an 80' x 20' screen draped between two 10-story buildings.

A laser art exhibit was held early in 1979 in Palm Springs, California. The event sponsored by the University of Cincinnati's laser laboratory included displays of laser design, painting, sculpture, etching, ceramics, lapidary and holography. The exhibit is the fifth arranged by Dr. Leon Goldman; others have been in Cincinnati, San Diego, Atlanta and Buffalo.

More than thirty years have passed since the Hungarian-born physicist Dennis Gabor developed the theory of holography while he worked at the Rugby Electrical Company in Scotland. Twenty-three years later his discovery won for Dr. Gabor the Nobel Prize in Physics. The original communication which appeared in "Nature" in May, 1948, eventually gave to the world a revolutionary method of three-dimensional photography. It gave to scientists and engineers a powerful and versatile tool. At the time of Dr. Gabor's discovery, however, there were no high-intensity, coherent light sources, or photographic emulsions of sufficiently high resolution to develop the new method of photography.

In 1948 Dr. Gabor did make some experimental holograms using a filtered mercury-vapor lamp as his light source. The images were small and blurred but they demonstrated that, in practice, his theory worked.

Invention of the laser in 1960 revived interest in Dr. Gabor's technique and the first laser holograms were produced in 1962 by Emmett Leith and Juris Upatnieks at the University of Michigan. These two scientists reproduced Gabor's earlier experiments with the new laser and overcame some of the difficulties of the original 'in-line' technique. Their invention of the so-called 'off-axis' holography marks the moment when holography began to make giant strides.

During the last fifteen years holography achieved universal appeal. It captured the imaginations of scientists, artists and laypeople, — of anyone who had the opportunity to view a three-dimensional image produced holographically.

A hologram contains all the visual information about the object (scene) recorded. But it does not show a conventional image. It appears to be an almost clear piece of glass or film until the recorded information is played back by illuminating the hologram with appropriate 'reconstructing' light: then the 3-D image of the object is seen with true depth and parallax.

The first holograms were played back with laser light and the 3-D image appeared behind the hologram. To the viewer, he appeared to be looking through a window frame. At the opening of the new General Motors building in New York City in 1968 four large (18″ x 24″) holograms were displayed. These were among the first holograms used promotionally and seen by the general public.

Human beings were shown holographically first in 1967 by L. D. Siebert of the Conductron Corporation. He used a pulsed ruby laser to make these first holograms of human subjects.

Another type of holographic system, 'white light reflection holography', was invented in 1961 by Yu. N. Denisyuk of the Soviet Union. This type of hologram does not require laser light for playback and the 3-D image appears to be floating in space between the hologram and the viewer. Since lasers were not available to Professor Denisyuk, his results were rather primitive. This technique, based on the Lippmann-Bragg effect, was further developed by Drs. George W. Stroke and A. E. Labeyrie in 1966. Today, white light reflection holography has been perfected by Prof. Denisyuk as he demonstrated at the 1977 Metrology Conference in Strasbourg, France.

In 1968, Dr. Stephen A. Benton of Polaroid Corporation developed the 'white light transmission hologram' which could be viewed either in sunlight, by bare incandescent bulb, flashlight, or even a candle. Early efforts produced a spectrum effect similar to the hologram of Michael York which was used in the film "Logan's Run." Because of the prismatic coloration this type of hologram was referred to as a 'rainbow hologram'. In 1974 Benton perfected a developing process to improve image quality and brightness and the year after he devised a process which produced a black-and-white (achromatic) effect. Because of the ease of playback the Benton-type hologram has great potential in display holography, but it must be noted that they show either horizontal or vertical parallax only.

In 1968, Gerry Pethick, an artist, produced a vibration isolation system for making holograms. Since a hologram is a record of interference patterns, the slightest vibration of the holographic setup will obliterate these patterns and no hologram will be recorded on the emulsion. Pethick's inexpensive 'sandbox' design made holography more accessible to laypeople.

Combining the techniques of white light transmission holography with the integral holography technique developed by R. V. Pole at IBM, Lloyd Cross and Dave Schmidt began work, in 1972, to develop a commercially feasible method for holographic movies. Their success led to the formation of Multi-plex Co. of San Francisco. Cross also designed and built the optical printers needed to produce thousands of integral holograms from an original master. Cross and integral holography played a leading role in bringing holography into public view. The first white-light viewable holographically processed movie, circular in form, 45 seconds in length, was commissioned by the New York Art Alliance, Inc. It was titled, "Sam Rivers" by the South African artist, Selwyn Lissack. In 1974 Salvador Dali commissioned a 45-second holo-movie of himself and his wife, Gala. Since that time integral (multiplex) holography has become a spectacular success as a sales tool for trade shows.

Just as visual experience of kinetic light art cannot be conveyed by still photographs, so reproductions in two-dimensional form in this book cannot transmit the experience produced by holograms. Holograms must be viewed. They must be experienced first hand.

The first holographic art exhibition was held in 1970 at the Cranbrook Academy of Art, Bloomfield Hills, Michigan. Twenty-seven holograms were shown by Cross, Alan Lite, Pethick and others. An exhibition of holograms, "N-Dimensional Space" was held in 1972 at the Finch College Museum of Art. "Holography '75: The First Decade" was produced by Joseph Burns, Jr. and Rosemary Jackson. It was presented at the International Center of Photography in New York City.

In March, 1976 "Holography: The 3-Dimensional Medium" was presented by the Stockholm Cultural Administration at the House of Culture, Stockholm, Sweden. This event was produced by Rosemary Jackson, Director of the Museum of Holography, and Jody Burns, President of the New York Art Alliance, Inc., and Sven Lidbeck of AVC, Stockholm.

Two important exhibition of holograms produced by HOLOCO members were shown at the Royal Academy of Arts, London, England, in March 1977 and January-March, 1978.

Up to now, the world's so far largest exhibition of display holograms, "Alice in the Light World: An Exhibition of Holography Today" was held in August, 1978 at a department store in Tokyo, Japan. The 90-piece show represented the work of outstanding holographers from all over the world; examples of all major hologram types were displayed. The two-week run was viewed by more than fifty thousand people. This exhibition was sponsored by the Asahi Shimbun, one of Japan's largest newspapers and was supported by the Japan Society of Applied Physics, the Japan Society of Image Arts and Sciences, Holomedia, Inc., Toshiba Electric Co., and Nippon Electric Co.

Centers for holographic education are growing in number. A listing of the better known ones follows.

The Museum of Holography located in New York City (11 Mercer Street) was founded in 1976 by Rosemary H. Jackson to provide a focal point for the growing public interest in holography. The Museum produces three to four exhibitions annually which point up the latest developments in holographic art and science. The Museum has a permanent collection of over 300 historic and state-of-the-art works, provides lectures, maintains a reference library and publishes a monthly journal, "holosphere." The Bookstore is the world's largest retail outlet for books on holography and all types of holograms. The Museum's traveling exhibition of holograms, "Through the Looking Glass," has been on view in the USA and Canada. The Museum also publishes "Who's Who in Display Holography," a cross-referenced guide to holographers and holographic companies. Open Wednesday through Sunday between noon and 6 p.m., Thursdays until 9 p.m.

The Odyssey Image Center (OIC) at 8853 Sunset Boulevard in Hollywood, California, offers a gallery of holograms available for view by the public. Open from 3 p.m. to 3 a.m., daily. Readers in the Chicago area should visit Gallery 1134 (1134 W. Washington Blvd., Chicago, Illinois). Exhibitions change every few weeks. Open daily 11 a.m. to 6 p.m., except Monday.

In Canada, Fringe Research (1179A King Street, Toronto, Ontario) has been active in organizing holography exhibitions. The Hologram Place, London's first permanent hologram gallery and shop, opened in November, 1978, at 138 Gloucester Avenue, London, NW1, England, The gallery features work by outstanding American holographers, as well as holograms made by the British firm HOLOCO.

While far from complete, this book attempts to outline the creative work being done with lasers and the experimental development of the laser medium. It is the author's aim to stimulate interest in laser art in general and to create a desire to seek new approaches to the medium. Laser light is a tool, it is no more an artist than paint is the painter or a violin the musician. The laser experimenter plays the part of editor-selector-composer. Finding a satisfactory image is a joy and a struggle. Let the experimenter enjoy the process of discovery in this most exciting medium. We are still exploring it and if it is true that artistry takes place at the point of interaction with the medium, then the question: "Is 'laser art' Art?" can be answered in the affirmative.

LASERS AND LASER LIGHT

Light is a form of radiation. It travels in a wave-like motion, the crests and troughs at right angles to the direction of travel. The distance from one crest to the next is the wavelength and every color has its own. White light, it should be noted, contains all colors of the visible spectrum.

Before the invention of the laser there was no source of spectrally pure and coherent light. Light from the sun or an electric bulb results from the spontaneous emission of radiation from an excited atom. The atom excited by an energy source radiates its excess energy spontaneously as light of measurable wavelength. The time and direction of the atom's radiation are random and unpredictable. Light from an ordinary source, therefore, because it is composed of many different wavelengths, out of step with each other, is considered incoherent.

Coherent light is monochromatic, composed of waves of identical length, in step and in unchanging relationship with each other. The narrow light beam from a laser comes close to this ideal but not even laser light is perfectly coherent.

As is generally known by now, the acronym *laser* is derived from Light Amplification by Stimulated Emission of Radiation, but the device commonly referred to as a laser is not so much an amplifier of light as an oscillator which generates light. *(It is needful now to introduce technical material which, while necessary for an understanding of how lasers work, is not a must for the non-technical reader, the one who wishes only to use laser light in any of its numerous applications.)* An electronic oscillator may be considered an amplifier which supplies its own signal. When the power is turned on, the first pulse of current creates a random signal which is amplified. Part of the amplifier output is then fed back to its input in correct phase. To produce oscillations resonance at a selected frequency is necessary. The feedback from amplifier output to input enables the amplifier to achieve a resonant signal which produces and maintains oscillations. Amplification is necessary to compensate for internal losses and enable the amplifier to continue to operate as an oscillator.

In a laser the resonant system is a long and thin tube with mirrors at each end. This so-called *optical cavity* contains the *lasing* medium, a mixture, for example, of helium and neon that is excited by an electrical discharge. Excitation is possible either by direct current (dc) similar to that in a neon sign, or by radio frequency waves (rf). The light traveling down the *discharge tube* (the optical cavity) is reflected by the end mirrors many times and makes many journeys back and forth in the tube. It is amplified by laser action, an atomic process. Since the tube and the mirrors form an optical resonant cavity, the optical path length between successive reflections at a mirror must be of an integral number of wavelengths to produce reinforcement of the wave by resonance. One of the mirrors is only partially silvered, so that some fraction of the radiation escapes to provide the output of the laser. Only light whose multiples of half a wavelength fit exactly between the mirrors is allowed to escape from the laser. Thus, standing waves are established between the mirrors. It is this resonant quality of the optical cavity which gives laser light its spectral purity.

The **helium-neon** (He-Ne) gas laser gives off a continuous wave of highly coherent red light at 633 nm (nanometer) wavelength. The narrow output beam emerges inherently well collimated and highly directional because only the light on the axis between the mirrors can escape from the laser.

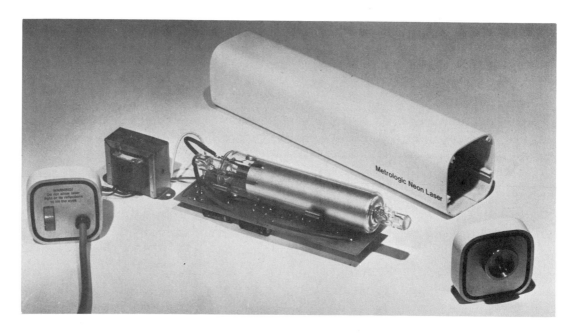

Component parts of a He-Ne gas laser.
(Courtesy Metrologic Instruments, Inc.)

Lasers that employ ions as the active medium produce continuous output in the visible part of the electromagnetic spectrum. The **argon** ion gas laser is more powerful than the He-Ne version. It is capable of emitting light in various wavelengths of blue and green and can be tuned to the desired wavelength.

The **krypton** ion gas laser is almost identical to the argon laser except that the discharge tube is filled with krypton gas. This laser can emit red, yellow, green, and blue simultaneously, or singly, with the use of a prism. By filling the discharge tube with a mixture of argon and krypton an almost white output beam can be obtained.

While the above described gas lasers emit a continuous beam of light which can be switched on and off like a light bulb, **ruby** lasers, on the other hand, emit very short bursts of light.

Ruby is the first material ever to demonstrate lasing action (1960). A small rod of synthetic ruby was 'pumped' by powerful bursts of light from a flash-tube, like the 'strobe' light used by photographers. The end faces of the ruby rod were polished flat, parallel and normal to the axis. Both end faces were silvered, one only partially so, to form a resonant cavity. As the optical pumping rate was increased the first few spontaneously emitted photons stimulated a chain reaction in the ruby rod. Eventually enough energy was available to overcome losses in the system and an intense pulse of red (694.3 nm) light emerged from the partially silvered end of the ruby rod.

The short duration of the ruby laser pulse makes it possible to record holograms without the vibration isolation equipment needed with gas lasers. Ruby lasers have two modes of operation. These are the 'long pulse' or 'regular lasing mode' (0.1 to 0.5 millisecond duration) and the 'short pulse' or 'Q-switch mode' (less than 0.1 microsecond duration). Portrait holograms of living subjects require a Q-switched ruby laser.

All the preceding are the most widely used lasers for the applications described in this book. More sophisticated, expensive and high-power laser systems are used to produce laser etchings and laser sculptures. While neodymium-YAG and CO_2 lasers are used in research and industry, they are seldom available to the artist inasmuch as they require stringent safety precautions.

To sum up: laser light is quite different from light normally encountered. Laser beams are narrow, pencil like, well collimated and highly directional. The light is monochromatic, meaning light of a single color. It is the coherence of laser light, the one previously unobtainable light property, that makes it such an important source of light. A well known and easily observable characteristic of laser light — due to its coherence — is its granular appearance upon reflection from or transmission through a diffuse surface.

When a He-Ne laser beam is expanded with a short focus lens and projected on a wall, a piece of paper, or a ground glass, the illuminated surface appears speckled with bright and dark regions which dance around as the diffuse surface or the observer slowly moves around. The speckled appearance is caused by interference effects of the elementary waves emanating from each element of the scattering surface. Since a scattering surface has completely

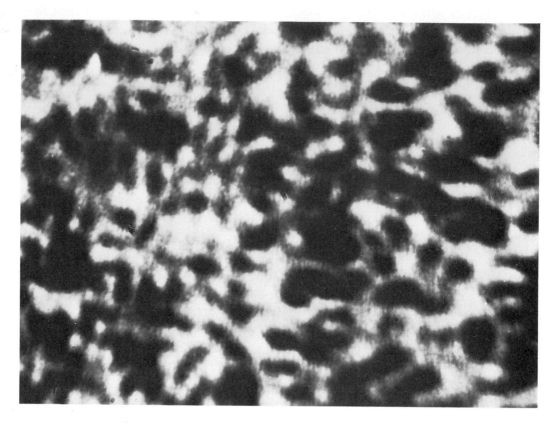

This is a 500x enlargement of the speckle pattern resulting from photographing a laser illuminated diffuse surface. (Courtesy G.E. Maddux, Air Force Flight Dynamics Laboratory, Wright-Patterson AFB.)

random characteristics the observed speckle pattern also has random appearance. The random interference field exists at all points in space between the scattering surface and the observer. The eyes see the granularity sharply, with or without spectacles, from any distance and any angle. Laser speckle has been a nuisance in coherent systems and in holography. A great amount of research has been done to reduce or eliminate its disturbing effects.

Laser Safety

High-power lasers are used in industry, in surgery, and even in static and kinetic art exhibits. They are used also to etch plastics and create laser sculptures. It is essential, therefore, that all persons exposed to laser hazards be knowledgeable about laser safety.

The experimental work described in this book can all be done with lasers in the 1.0 to 5.0 mW range. Except for holograms, a He-Ne laser in the 0.5 to 1.0 mW range is able to produce lasergrams and optical transforms with short exposure times. With ordinary caution these lasers are safe, but to insure safety at a possibly later date, when one might be working with medium- and high-power lasers, safety procedures should be followed at all times. Good working habits should be developed from the beginning. For examples, here are a few:

1) Treat all lasers and laser beams with respect. Never look into the laser's output window even when the unit is turned off.

2) Never point the laser beam near anyone's eyes. To protect passers-by cover all the room's windows.

3) Remove all superfluous and highly reflective objects from the beam's possible path. These include shiny tools, glassware, mirrors and glass-covered art on walls.

4) Adequate grounding should be provided for the laser case, and the laser should never be operated without a protective cover.

5) Never leave a laser unattended while it is activated. If it is not in use disconnect the power.

6) If eye-protecting devices are recommended for a particular laser do not rely on ordinary sunglasses.

7) If the presentation of laser art involves the active use of a laser, as in laser light shows, discotheques and the viewing of certain types of holograms, be extremely conscious of the people in the audience. Their protection from laser hazards is your responsibility!

LASER LIGHT GENERATED IMAGES

Painting with laser light will appeal to those interested in the symbolic and non-objective creation of images.

Laser Light Environment

It is possible to produce structures of light beams by reflecting a laser beam from mirrors, highly polished metal surfaces, or plastic sheets coated with a layer of reflecting material. Thus, a laser beam can be used for producing, via multiple reflections, a three-dimensional environment of beams of light. One way to make a laser beam visible in air is to fill the air through which the beam passes with some smoke. Steam and aerosol spray have also been used and the beam remains visible for as long as the air-borne particles remain suspended. In water, the path of the beam can be seen with the help of additives such as sodium fluorescein, hypo (photographic fixing salt) or liquid detergent.

Writing with Lasers

Instead of making the beam path visible, laser generated images can be projected on a wall or screen. Usually a darkened room is necessary when the images are projected on an opaque surface. When the projection comes from behind a translucent screen, the image can be viewed in a semi-darkened room. When rear-projection laser images are viewed in a completely darkened room, the images often appear to be suspended in space.

A laser beam, when projected on a screen, appears as a brilliant spot of light. To move this spot one may move the entire laser apparatus. It is much more practical, however, to intercept the beam with a small, hand-held, front-surface mirror and by quick manipulation of the mirror create abstract line-patterns on the screen. These patterns can then be recorded with a camera. Low-power lasers (He-Ne, 1.0 mW) require a fast film, such as Kodak Tri-X and a wide open lens (f/2). To make the photograph, darken the room, open the shutter, "write" the laser pattern and then close the shutter.

Spirograms

In place of the hand-held mirrors just described, two mirrors attached to small motors may be used to create interesting and repeatable patterns (spirograms).

A circular scan pattern can be generated by one, so-called, wobbulating mirror. The wobbulation of the mirror is caused by its non-perpendicular alignment with respect of the axis of the motor shaft. The incident laser beam is inclined at a fixed angle relative to the axis of rotation of the tilted mirror. The angle of incidence, however, between the beam and the tilted mirror varies in accordance with the instantaneous position of the rotating mirror. This variation results in the reflected beam forming a conical scan. If a viewing screen is positioned perpendicular to the axis of the conical scan, the reflected laser beam will describe a bright circle on the screen.

Sinusoidal deflection of a laser beam can be achieved with two small plane mirrors which rotate at equal speeds in opposite directions. Both mirrors are slightly inclined with relation to their axes of rotation but the axes themselves are parallel to each other. The block diagram shows the optical setup.

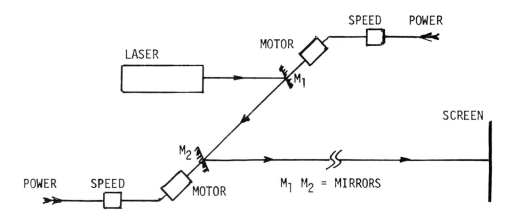

Counter-rotating mirrors as light deflectors

The two mirrors are so positioned that the emerging beam from the first scanning (wobbulating) mirror is incident upon the second. If the motors rotating the mirrors are interconnected in such a manner as to produce synchronous and in-phase rotation, then the circular deflections of the laser beam produced by each mirror are mutually cancelled and the scanning movement of the beam is a back-and-forth one along a straight line. In our setup an individual drive for each mirror was provided, with provision for speed adjustment of the drive motors to insure synchronous movement of the mirrors in correct phase relation.

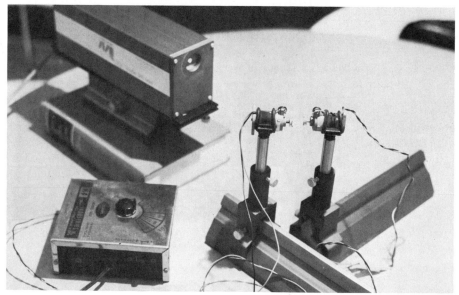

Spirogram experimental setup

Many other scan patterns can be obtained by (a) varying the mirror tilt angles, (b) the mirror rotation speeds, (c) the mirror rotation phase angles. Four of the Lissajous patterns (spirograms) obtained with the described setup are shown.

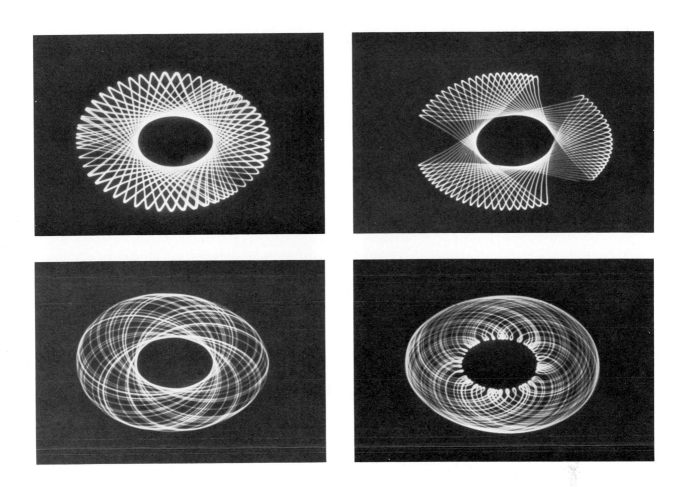

Samples of scan patterns (spirograms)

Visual Display of Sound

It is possible, with simple apparatus, to produce a light pattern for each single or combination of tones presented to the apparatus. With sound one can activate either a very thin metal plate, a drumhead, a thin sheet of rubber or plastic stretched on a frame. These surfaces can be excited by nearby talking or singing, by making sounds through nearby loudspeakers, or by directly coupled audio transducers. If a small, featherweight mirror were affixed to any of these surfaces and a laser beam bounced off the mirror onto a wall or screen, one could observe, in real time, visual images typical of the acoustical activity. The system is shown in the block diagram.

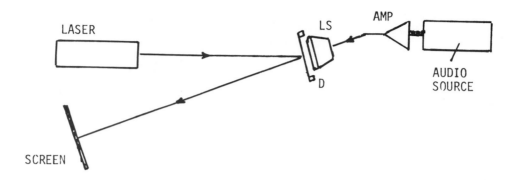

Visual display of sound dynamics

Observe the Lissajous figures when the sounds remain constant and the frequency-dependence of the patterns as the tone is changed. See how the patterns are amplitude-dependent, and note the effect of pitch and timbre. Watch the endless patterns created by the musical sounds and the vibrating medium to which the mirror is affixed. Patterns such as spirals, rings, flower petals, webs, clouds, textures, vortices, diamonds, sunbursts, weaves and turbulences are formed — the list is endless.

The diaphragm, *D*, is stretched in a suitable frame and a loudspeaker, *LS*, is mounted concentrically with the diaphragm. The loudspeaker is connected to the output of an audio signal generator/amplifier system. The diaphragm may be a thin plastics sheet (Saran-Wrap) with a mirror surface, such as vacuum deposited aluminum. The laser beam is directed toward the mirror surface of the diaphragm from which it reflects to a viewing screen. The diaphragm is made to vibrate by sound pressure waves from the loudspeaker. The vibration of the diaphragm will distort the mirror surface which will then produce a characteristic light pattern on the screen. The pattern will appear to be a line figure because the retinal retention of the eye is much longer than the time required to scan an audio signal pattern.

An alternate system utilizes two loudspeakers. In this modification the diaphragms are made of framed and stretched thin rubber sheets which are optically non-reflective. Very thin glass or plastic mirrors are glued to the rubber diaphragms, D_1 and D_2. The audio system feeds a crossover network which is connected to a high-frequency and low-frequency speaker. The laser beam is first reflected from the diaphragm which responds to high sound frequencies and then to and from the diaphragm which responds to low sound frequencies. The size of the pattern so produced on the screen will be propor-

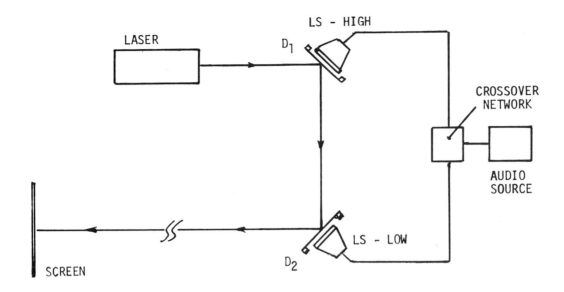

An alternate system for the visual display of sound

tional to the amplitude of the sound and the shape of the pattern will be a complex function of the sound. Several of these patterns are shown in the chapter on "Laser Theatre."

Light Caustics

The space between the laser source and the screen may be used by the artist to modify the beam and produce light images on the viewing screen. The objects placed in this space are called modulators. The imagery depends on the optical activity of the modulator. It may involve reflection, refraction, interference, dispersion and diffraction. The use of polarization filters add another factor for control.

The artist regards laser light and its modulators as a compositional instrument. The modulator is the device which sculpts the laser beam in space and the artist has complete freedom to frame the image. By moving the screen away from the modulator the projection grows larger on the screen. Still further away, the artist may choose to cut out only part of the total projection. The screen can be moved physically up or down, right or left, the same way a photographer works in the darkroom when cropping an enlarged negative. Screen, in this context, means an opaque or translucent projection screen, or a photosensitive film or paper if a permanent record of the image is desired. Of course, the image can be directly photographed from the projection screen. Flexibility in image control is the result of searching out and/or creating appropriate modulators. Exploring and experimenting with modulators in search of beautiful abstract compositions involves an element of chance. While chance often aids discovery, discovery rarely results from chance alone. This is a visual art source that seems inexhaustible!

When unidirectional light is passed through an optically irregular substance it produces a field of waves moving in different directions. These so-called light caustics form exciting geometric patterns on screens or photographic plates placed in the field. A familiar caustic is the changing pattern on the bottom of a swimming pool in bright sunlight. To demonstrate caustics in the home or lab, laser light is directed through irregular bathroom glass on to a wall. These caustics show lines, cusps, corners, so-called swallowtails, elliptic umbilics, hyperbolic umbilics and other shapes.

These structures of bright images are created by expanding the laser beam with a short focal length lens and placing a modulator close to the laser in the divergent beam.

Light modulators made of fractured glass pieces produce many interesting effects. Heat treating a thick piece of clear plastic will result occasionally in a useful modulator. Industrial plastic or molded glass objects are often modulators, producing delightful images. An easily made refraction type modulator can be made by applying, irregularly, rapid setting plastic liquids to a plate glass surface such as a photographic cover glass. The author found that Duco household cement on glass or Plexiglas works well. Beautiful effects can be achieved even from an irregular water droplet on a flat glass plate. A drop of linseed oil between two cover glasses leaves an interesting tracing when the glass plates are pulled apart. Both plates can serve as modulators.

The process of crystallization is one of nature's wonders. Crystallization can be slowed by the addition of a synthetic resin. A thin layer of solution should be applied on a cover glass. One can experiment with vitamins: B_2, D and E; or Rhodamine B, a fluorescent dye. Or, try liquid crystals. There are many, many others.

Interference patterns created by a laser beam reflected from an aluminized ripple-glass surface can be spectacular. Entirely different effects are achieved if, after reflection, the beam is projected through a microscope's eyepiece onto the screen.

Kodak Panalure paper is best to make black-and-white prints directly from color negatives. This panchromatic paper may also be used to record the laser generated images without first photographing them. The result, of course, is a negative image on paper. The transposition of the tone-values transposes the relationships also and some unusual effects can be achieved with this technique.

Motion may be introduced by moving the image producing elements (modulators) individually or by moving them as a group. The individual elements of a Light Mobile can, theoretically, describe an infinite number of paths. The moving light images projected on a screen are determined by the movement of the modulators, and the shapes given to the fixed and moving reflectors. The various elements can be made to perform rotational, pendular (planar) and pendular (torsional) motion. If independent, variable speed motors and other drivers are used separately with each of the modulating elements, then constantly new images are created which never repeat. Aluminum or silver coated plastic sheet permits the construction of lightweight armatures easily moved by miniature motors. The author produced numerous kinetic laser paintings with the help of small, variable speed motors, featherweight mirrors, thin rubber sheets, diffraction gratings, Fresnel lenses and prisms, all inexpensively obtained from Edmund Scientific Co. (Barrington, New Jersey 08007, U.S.A.).

To sum up, the following are some of the ways to use lasers in producing static and kinetic light art:

1. *Laser Light Environment*

    Imagery: Laser beam paths in three-dimensional space
    Technique: Multiple reflection by plane and curved mirrors
    Laser source: Usually He-Ne, also argon and krypton
    Optical setup:

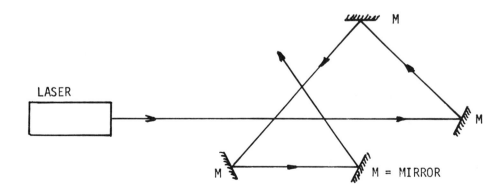

2. *Writing with Lasers*

Imagery: Moving laser beam spot displayed on a screen
Technique: Laser beam deflected by small hand-held mirror
Laser source: He-Ne
Optical setup:

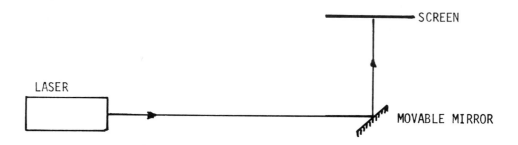

3. *Spirograms*

Imagery: Lissajous patterns projected on a screen
Technique: Laser beam deflected by two motor-driven wobbulating mirrors
Laser source: He-Ne
Optical setup:

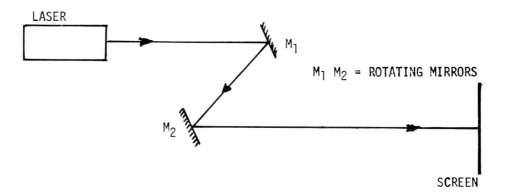

4. *Visual Display of Sound*

Imagery: Simple and complex patterns created in response to sound
Technique: Laser beam deflected by one or more sound-modulated mirrors

Laser source: He-Ne, argon, krypton
Optical setup:

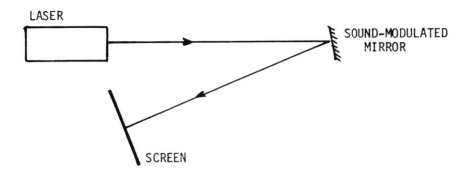

5. *Light Caustics*

Imagery: Complicated interference patterns projected on a screen
Technique: Refractive light modulators (RLM) intercept laser beam
Laser source: Usually He-Ne; also argon or krypton for large screens
Optical setup:

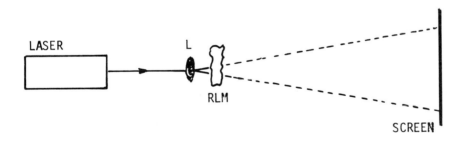

6. *Optical Transforms*

Imagery: Diffraction patterns projected on a screen
Technique: Expanded laser beam intercepted by a diffracting aperture, *A*.
    Details given elsewhere in the book.
Laser source: Low-power He-Ne.
Optical setup:

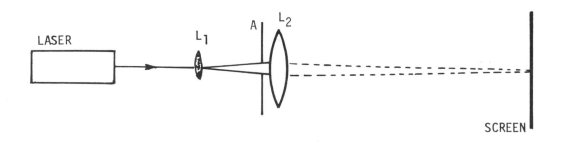

7. *Laser Theatre*

Imagery: A combination of all the above except #1 and #2
Technique: Described elsewhere in the book
Laser source: Usually argon and/or krypton

Randy James: *Laser Light Pattern.* The unspread beam of a 5 mW He-Ne laser was reflected off a dented piece of stainless steel. (Courtesy Multiplex Co.)

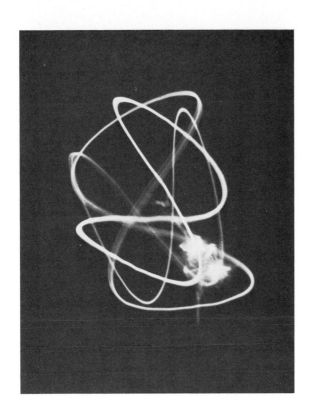

T. Kallard. *Laser 'Writing' Created With Hand-held Mirror.*

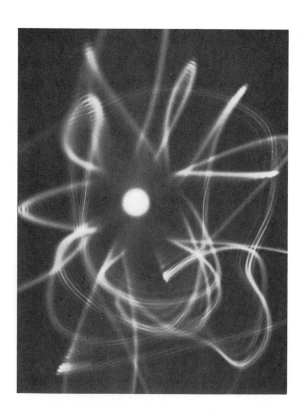

T. Kallard. *Laser Light Designs Created With a Moving Fresnel Lens.*

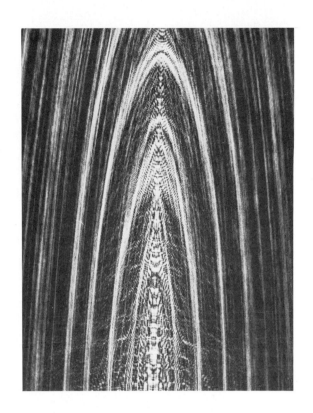
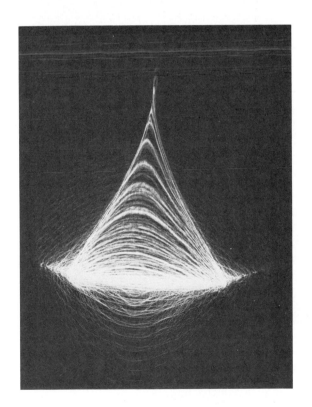
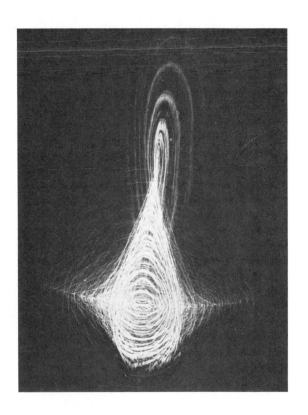

T. Kallard. *Lasergrams Created With a Fresnel Lens.*

Leon Goldman, M.D. *Laser Free Form Design.* Free form design produced by argon laser swept over a Kodachrome transparency picture of a tattoo of the forearm almost completely erased by a ruby laser treatment. (From the Laser Laboratory of the Medical Center of the University of Cincinnati.)

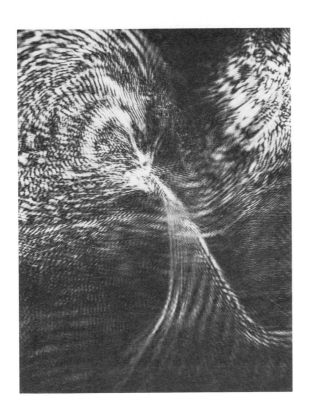 

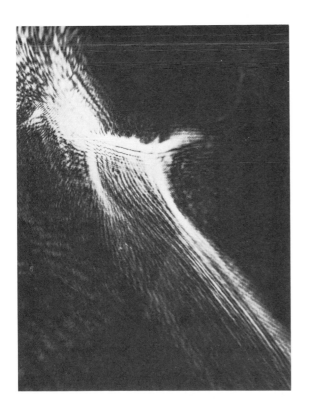 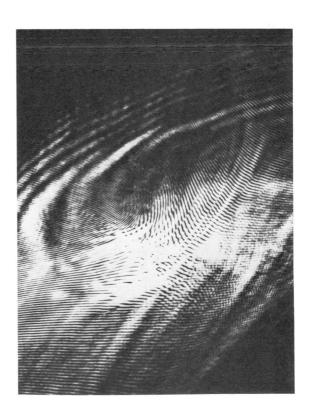

T. Kallard. *Light Caustics.* (Recorded on Kodak Panatomic-X film.)

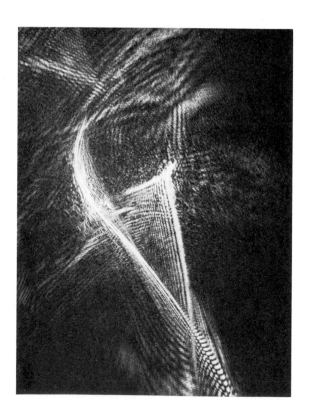 

T. Kallard. *Light Caustics.* (Recorded on Kodak Panatomic-X film.)

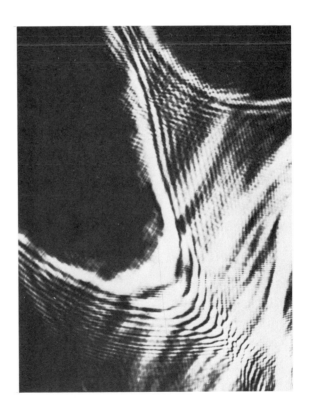

T. Kallard. *Light Caustics.* (Recorded on Kodak Panatomic-X film.)

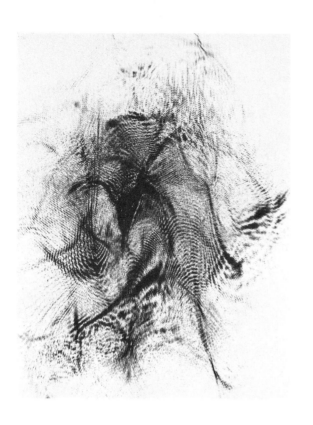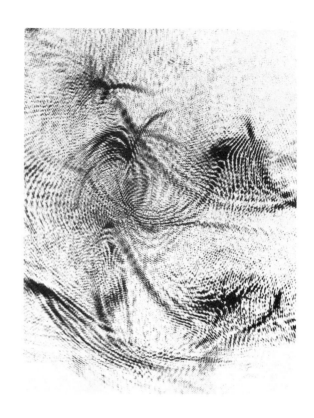

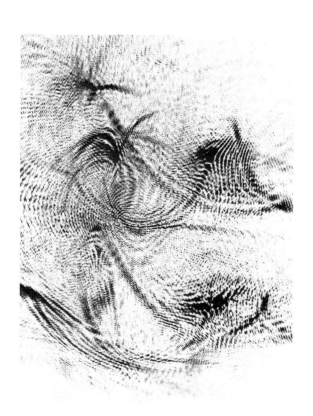

T. Kallard. *Light Caustics.* (Projected on Kodak Panalure paper.)

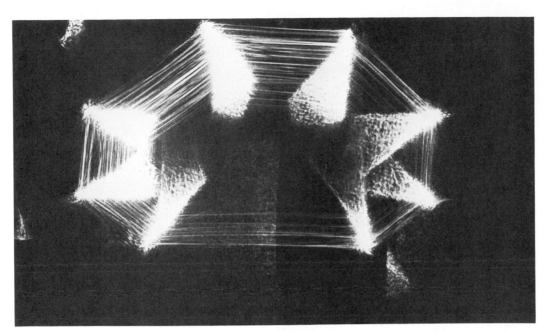

Louis M. Brill. *Lead-glass Crystal I.* (Courtesy Wavefronts; photo Bruce Dantzkar.)

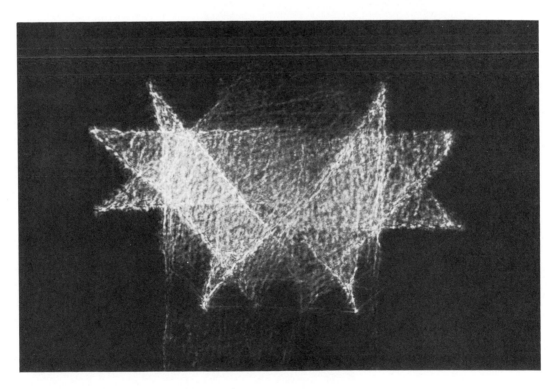

Louis M. Brill. *Lead-glass Crystal II.* (Courtesy Wavefronts; photo Bill Kaunitz.)

Peter Van Riper. *Planet Plant.* Laser
diffusion cast on organic form.

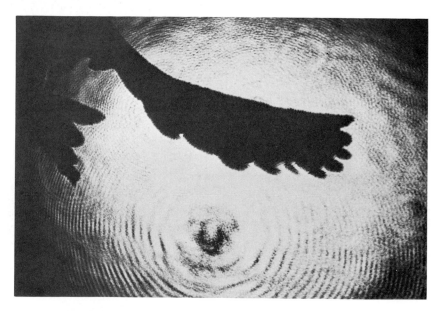

Peter Van Riper. *Night Elk.* Laser diffusion cast on organic form.

Peter Van Riper. *Laser Lace.* Laser diffraction through the focal point of a plastic sphere.

Leon Goldman, M.D. *Release from Bondage.* A laser sculpture in acrylic; black materials included in the mold. Ruby, CO_2 and argon lasers were used. "Best of Show," San Francisco, December, 1978, Academy of Dermatology Art Show. (From the Laser Laboratory of the Medical Center of the University of Cincinnati.)

LASER THEATRE

It is assumed that, by now, the nature and characteristics of laser light are generally understood by the reader. To review briefly, however, the narrow beam of light from a medium-power laser is bright enough to rival light from the sun. Its power, even after numerous mirrored reflections, even after refraction through prisms, is ample and yields a brilliant spot of light when finally reflected onto a screen.

We come now, however, to a consideration of lasers as the medium in a new and expanding art form: Laser theatre. Visualize, if you will, that needle-like light beam; see it reflected from one mirror into another and from the other onto a screen. The sharp, hot spot of light on the screen will, of course, respond to the slightest motion of either mirror. Up or down, side to side, in swooping arcs or tight circles, the range and direction of the laser spot is almost limitless, or, more accurately, its limitations depend only on the talent and dexterity of the people moving the mirrors.

But why must the laser's mirrors be moved by people? Why not by electrically powered mechanical devices designed to move the reflecting surfaces in any chosen direction? And considering the advanced state of the electronic arts, why not electronic control of the mechanical devices?

Good questions all, and many of them already answered. At present, laser mirror motion is usually produced by a moving iron galvanometer, a high-speed galvanometer developed and patented by Jean Montagu and Pierre Brosens of General Scanning Incorporated, Watertown, Massachusetts. These instruments are among the fastest electro-mechanical devices known. They are able to move a reflected laser spot so quickly and so accurately that the image retention ability of the human eye perceives it not as a moving spot but a solid line.

Consider a spot reflected on a screen and being moved rapidly back and forth between points A and B at a speed of about twenty-five times per second. At this speed the eye no longer sees a spot but rather a continuous line. Reduce the mirrors' motion to about fifteen times per second and the line begins to flicker. While it is true that the operator of such a basic and elementary laser display can, if need be, reduce the speed of the moving spot in order to add some small detail, it is equally true that he must take great care. The price of detail achieved with too slow scanning speeds can be distracting flicker. The important thing to remember, however, is that it was now possible to form images. The General Scanning galvanometers with their associated mirrors and controls, were able to control not only the speed of the laser spot but its direction as well. A new art form was in the making.

Start with an artistic, electronics technician — no longer a contradiction in terms. Add the necessary equipment, a laser, mirrors and the high-speed galvanometers with all their complex control gear, and the operator was now in a position to project an image onto a screen. Further, he could keep the image there for as long as he was able to repeat the pattern of changes in the laser spot's direction, repeat it at precisely the right time and in the right sequence.

The difficulties involved with making these split-second changes in spot motion are obvious. The operator would have to be a robot — or become one. And assuming he could, certain anatomical changes would still be necessary: two hands were no longer enough to do the job. With sophistication, the galvanometers' control dials had become ever more numerous, more complex as the demand grew for more complex and even animated images.

Adding to the problems already in existence was the advent of color. Its quick acceptance in the television industry made it impossible for laser technicians to resist its lure. Thankfully, the problems color presented were not insurmountable. A multi-color laser's beam, refracted through a prism, would split into its component colors. The needed colors could then be isolated and each one controlled by its own pair of mirrors and galvanometers. The technique was based on knowledge already in existence, but the problem of the number of dials and knobs the laser operator now had to monitor was increased about fourfold. What one person had barely been able to do now required the skills of four prople, a coordinated team, practicing and rehearsing endlessly.

The effort required was so great, the personnel and the equipment so expensive, that producers of now possible laser shows in full color were reluctant to invest the large sums needed to put them on. It took a marriage between art and science to provide the solution. Expanding developments in computer technology made it possible to store electronic information on computer tape. It could be stored this way permanently and played back repeatedly. The artistic laserist could now, at his own pace and convenience, record his images on computer tape. For better control, he could even record each color separately. When it was time to show his work he merely set the tapes to play back, sat down in the audience and enjoyed the show with everyone else.

So, laser theatre was born. Copies of tapes could be made and the same show put on in different theatres at the same time. One technician was all that was needed to rack up the tape and push the "ON" botton. The quality of the performance was already there and improving rapidly with the convenience of pre-recorded tape. The artist/engineer laserist, when creating the show, could record purposely at a slow speed with the intention of playing back at a higher, normal speed — this to make possible the representation of fully animated figures, such as dancers in graceful motion, dragons breathing fire and water flowing coolly.

Lovelight

The first fully automated laser theatre performance was a musical called "Lovelight." It opened February 4, 1977 at the Boston Museum of Science's Charles Hayden Planetarium and was so well received that a second projection system was built and a simultaneous performance staged at the Metropole Theatre in London. The "Lovelight" tape is so completely automated that even the button pushing is activated by a special control track on the computer tape. A measure of its success may be taken from the fact that one scene from the show was used as a cover story in the May 1977 issue of the technical journal, *Laser Focus*. The show's content is highly advanced and expertly developed with narration, recorded music and elaborate imagery.

"Lovelight" was first produced by Interscan, an organization since disbanded. It was formed originally by the merger of two companies: General Scanning, Inc., of Watertown, Massachusetts and Intermedia Systems Corporation of Cambridge, Massachusetts. Gerd Stern, a founding member of USCO, the pioneer American kinetic-light art group, and president of Intermedia was the man responsible for production. Most of the visuals were created by Walter Gundy and Jennifer Morris of Cambridge, Massachusetts. Optical hardware was supplied by General Scanning, with much of the optical equipment of special design done by Jean Montagu, president of General Scanning. The image generating electronics and some of the other special equipment used was designed and supplied by Brian O'Brien, an independent Professional Engineer and laser innovator of Newton, Massachusetts. The three simplified block diagrams show Dr. O'Brien's automated projection system.
(Much of the foregoing material is the result of lengthy and enlightening communication with Dr. Brian O'Brien.)

Laser theatre systems will continue to advance despite the present limitation of their cost. A fully automated system with sufficient power for a medium sized theatre is likely to be in the $50,000 to $100,000 range but these are 1978 figures. In time, the cost of lasers and related computer equipment will go down. We look forward to that time because we have here what must be called something completely new: a happy marriage of Engineering with Art. The issue from this union will loom large in our future and be worth watching.

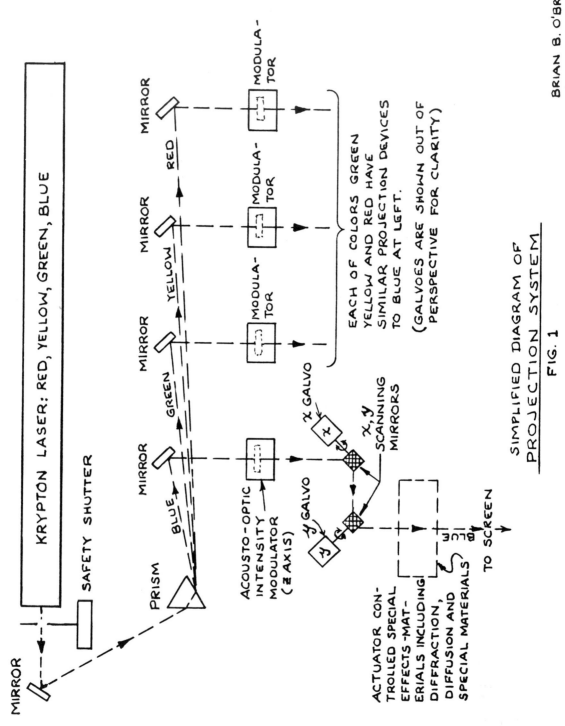

SIMPLIFIED DIAGRAM OF
PROJECTION SYSTEM

FIG. 1

BRIAN B. O'BRIEN, P.E.
NEWTON, MASS.

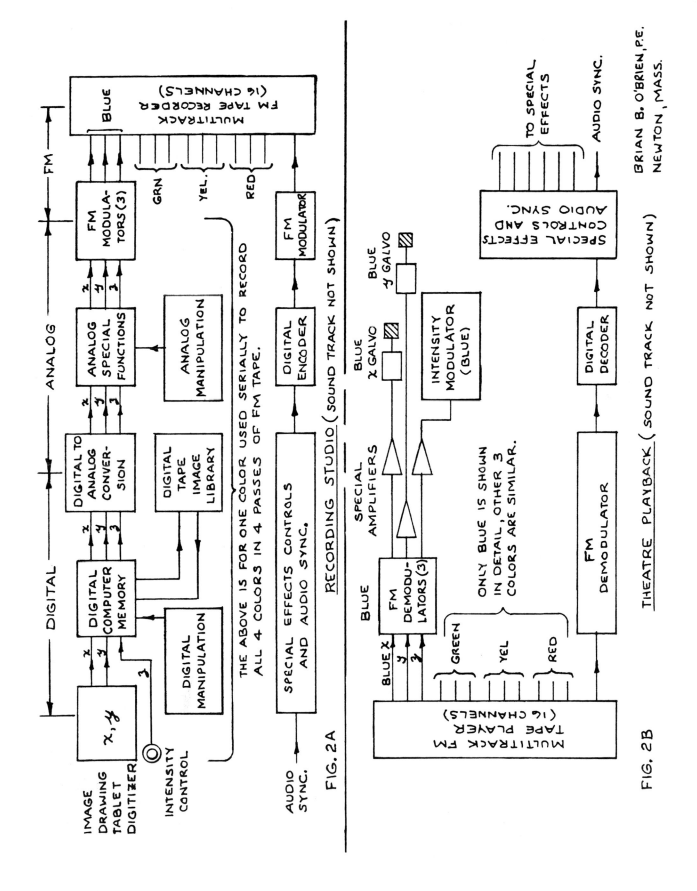

IMAGE DRAWING TABLET DIGITIZER

INTENSITY CONTROL

DIGITAL COMPUTER MEMORY

DIGITAL MANIPULATION

DIGITAL TO ANALOG CONVERSION

DIGITAL TAPE IMAGE LIBRARY

ANALOG SPECIAL FUNCTIONS

ANALOG MANIPULATION

FM MODULATORS (3)

MULTITRACK FM TAPE RECORDER (16 CHANNELS)

BLUE
GRN
YEL.
RED

DIGITAL · ANALOG · FM

SPECIAL EFFECTS CONTROLS AND AUDIO SYNC.

DIGITAL ENCODER

FM MODULATOR

AUDIO SYNC.

THE ABOVE IS FOR ONE COLOR USED SERIALLY TO RECORD ALL 4 COLORS IN 4 PASSES OF FM TAPE.

RECORDING STUDIO (SOUND TRACK NOT SHOWN)

FIG. 2A

MULTITRACK FM TAPE PLAYER (16 CHANNELS)

BLUE
GREEN
YEL
RED

FM DEMODULATORS (3)

SPECIAL AMPLIFIERS

ONLY BLUE IS SHOWN IN DETAIL, OTHER 3 COLORS ARE SIMILAR.

INTENSITY MODULATOR (BLUE)

BLUE X GALVO

BLUE Y GALVO

FM DEMODULATOR

DIGITAL DECODER

SPECIAL EFFECTS CONTROLS AND AUDIO SYNC.

TO SPECIAL EFFECTS

AUDIO SYNC.

THEATRE PLAYBACK (SOUND TRACK NOT SHOWN)

FIG. 2B

BRIAN B. O'BRIEN, P.E.
NEWTON, MASS.

Laserium

Ivan Dryer is the creator of *Laserium I, Laserium II,* and *Laserock,* and president of Laser Images Inc. Mr. Dryer spent 12 years directing, writing and editing documentaries, experimental and educational films and TV commercials before he started Laserium in late 1971. The idea for Laserium came after seeing a demonstration of a laser projection technique at the California Institute of Technology in 1970. He filmed the demonstration *(Laserimage)* but recognized that film could not begin to capture the vivid effect of live laser imagery.

It was Dryer's idea to choose a planetarium as the ideal environment for large scale laser shows. In 1971 he formed Laser Images Inc. to create *Laserium I: the Cosmic Laser Concert.* Laserium was presented at the Griffith Observatory in Los Angeles in November 1973 and since then has played in about a dozen United States centers, several cities in Canada, London, and in Kyoto, Japan, where a custom-designed laserium dome was constructed.

Because planetariums, like all educational facilities, can always use money, Laserium was welcomed at all of them. Laser concerts are a great source of extra funds. As of this writing over six million people have seen Laserium performances. The money from ticket sales is usually split between Laser Images and the exhibiting planetarium.

The system used in Laserium is built around a one-watt, krypton gas laser. The thin laser beam is passed through a prism which separates the laser's output into its component colors: red, yellow, green and blue. Each of these beams of color is processed via scanning mirrors, filters and modulators to produce complex multicolor images, seemingly suspended in the night sky of the planetarium dome.

Sound tracks and basic control signals are provided from a pre-recorded tape but the main laser projector signals are mixed and blended live. The automated part of the laser program constitutes 5 to 30 per cent of the imagery.

Laserium has no plot or story line. It is purely abstract. The shows are mostly improvised and no two are exactly alike. Perhaps this explains why over 50 per cent of its audiences are return customers.

The laser controller, called the laserist, sits in front of the control panel with its switches, dials and buttons. He works with a preconceived choreography of lights, colors and patterns. He has, however, full control as well as interpretational power to manually override the pre-set program, or to allow the lights and music to be electronically linked so that the light patterns correspond to the rhythms of the music and also to its volume. The laserist is free to repond to audience reaction when using the control console and to follow his own impulses while watching the display on the dome. He has no preview monitor. His hands are at home on the control board and he creates the imagery on the dome as he listens to the music. It is done in 'real time' and thus, the laserist, is a creative interpreter.

Performances are one hour in length. The music in "Laserium I" ranges from Johann Strauss and Corelli to Cal Tjader. There are several numbers by the Pink Floyd and some by Emerson, Lake and Palmer, and others. "Laserium II" is a celebration of American music composers and performers. John Philip Sousa, Kool and the Gang, Aaron Copland, Scott Joplin, Gary Wright, Timothy Randolph Clark and Stevie Wonder are represented. "Laserock" features Earth, Wind & Fire, Tangerine Dream, Jefferson Starship, Fleetwood Mac and many more.

Some of the Laserium and Laserock effects are truly hypnotic and despite the imagery being projected on the planetarium's dome, the illusion of three-dimensionality is convincing. The photographs reproduced here were taken by the author during live performances at the Hayden Planetarium in New York. Greg Weissman was the laserist. These illustrations cannot do justice to the color, the intensity and the excitement of the presentation. A 35-mm single-lens reflex camera was used with Kodak Tri-X film at f/2 with both wide-angle and normal lenses, all hand held; exposures ranged from ¼ to several seconds; development was 'pushed' 50 per cent. Flash is forbidden during the performance because it would disturb the audience. It would be pointless, in any event, since the intense light flash would wipe out the laser imagery displayed on the planetarium's dome.

Soleil

The *Soleil Laser Fantasia* is the creation of the founders and program builders, Bruce Rogers and Gary Levenberg, former students of the renowned contemporary composer, Iannis Xenakis. Rogers served as Xenakis' assistant for the Polytope de Cluny in Paris, France. The Polytope was Xenakis' original laser production. He used 600 xenon flashes and 8-channel sound track. Scheduled for one month, the Polytope had an extended run of 18 months from 1972 to 1974. Gary Levenberg studied with Xenakis at the Indiana University, where he also studied jazz improvisation with David Baker.

When he returned from Europe in 1974, Rogers met with Levenberg and the two began to plan their own laser production. They designed and assembled a laser system which toured extensively since March 1976. Coast-to-coast performances of the *Soleil Laser Music Spectacle* featured Rogers' and Levenberg's original electronic music and their laser light choreography. The "Spectacle" was designed to totally surround the audience with sound, color and movement. Soleil generates a small amount of smoke during the concerts which serves as a three-dimensional screen for the laser light.

The "Fantasia" employs two separate laser units to produce four differently colored laser beams. At the front of the hall a krypton gas laser projects brilliant blood-red color over the heads of the audience. An argon laser unit projects from the rear of the hall and produces three laser beams: blue, green and turquoise, which are aimed at a gigantic screen at the front of the auditorium.

For transforming the raw laser beam into the various flowing shapes and patterns used in the concert, a laser synthesizer, Lasyn, was designed by Soleil. At the control board of the Lasyn console sits Soleil's laser operator. At a touch of the laserist's hand, the Lasyn commands the laser beams to spin, to turn — literally to dance — and allows the highly trained laserist to follow the orchestra's conductor and interpret the music. The Soleil scanner and laser modulation equipment is able to expand a brilliant pinpoint of light into assorted images and shapes on the screen — even into written words. The Lasyn was designed to be a live laser performance instrument. Soleil also designed and built a tape playback system able to record laser programs created in Soleil's computer language, LITE.

July 4, 1976 was the highlight of Soleil's Bicentennial year. Soleil's performance from the top of the Washington Monument was an official part of the Bicentennial celebration for an estimated audience of four million. For this performance five high-power lasers were used. After the fireworks display, reputedly the largest in history, two of the lasers presented a specially commissioned program of laser writing and five-sided stars. The laser beams were seen as far away as twenty miles.

Among the spin-off benefits of the Star Wars movie craze are concerts, with a large orchestra playing "Music From Outer Space" along with a light show. Starting with Zubin Mehta and the Los Angeles Philharmonic at the Hollywood Bowl, some 40 to 50 concerts have been produced already. Soleil was involved with nearly 20 of these concerts and the "Symphony of the Stars" production became the largest and most performed of the works. It features the Chicago Festival Orchestra and the Soleil Laser Fantasia.

For Symphony of the Stars a krypton laser provided the red beam. An argon laser's output was split to provide blue and green beams. Also used were two xenon slide projectors with a manual dissolve unit and a 40' x 60' screen. Episode Lighting Co. provided orchestra lighting, follow spots, strobe lights, a mirror ball, four flame-throwers with adjustable flame up to 16 feet, and other special effects.

Each visual effect was carefully planned to follow the music and maintain audience interest during the two-hour concert. The show culminates with the "Close Encounters Suite" and for the battle scene during the "Star Wars Suite" all stops are pulled: Opposing laser ships fly around the screen firing and exploding. Flames shoot up, lights flash, bombs explode — and all of these closely coordinated with the music.

Laser images from *LOVELIGHT*, a laser musical produced by Interscan. (Photos courtesy Intermedia Systems Corp.)

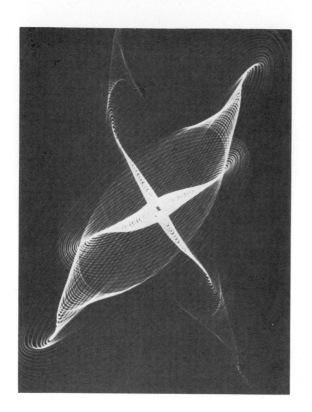

Live laser images from *LASERIUM* and *LASEROCK* produced by Laser Images, Inc. (Photos T. Kallard.)

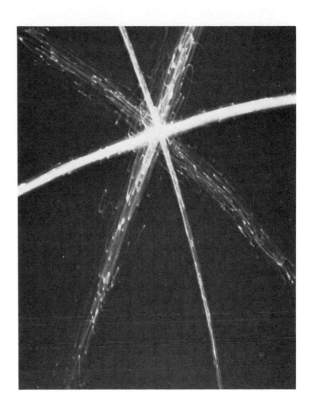

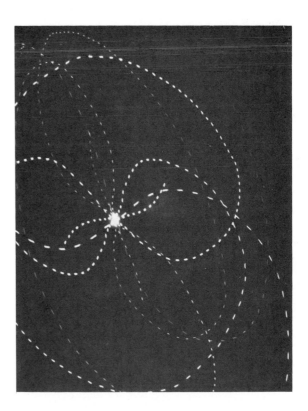

Live laser images from *LASERIUM* and *LASEROCK* produced by Laser Images, Inc. (Photos T. Kallard.)

 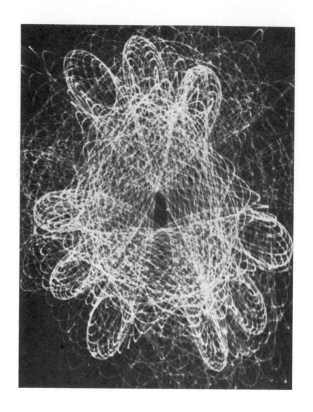

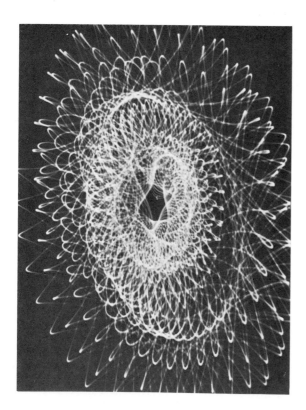 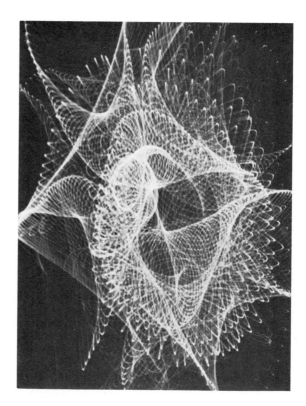

Live laser images from *LASERIUM* and *LASEROCK* produced by Laser Images, Inc. (Photos T. Kallard.)

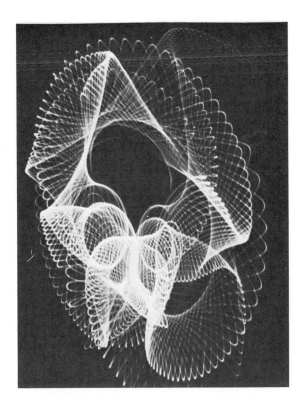
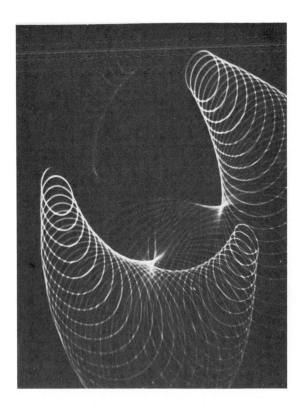

Live laser images from *LASERIUM* and *LASEROCK* produced by Laser Images, Inc. (Photos T. Kallard.)

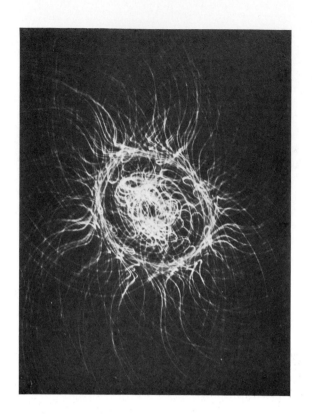
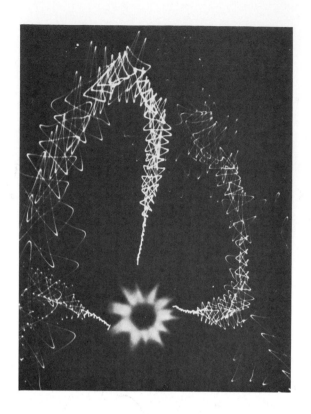
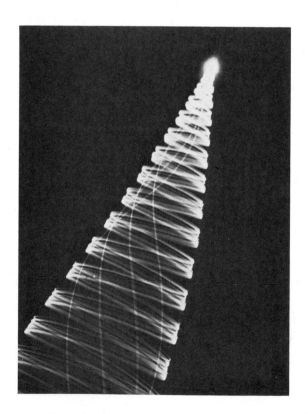

Live laser images from *LASERIUM* and *LASEROCK* produced by Laser Images, Inc. (Photos T. Kallard.)

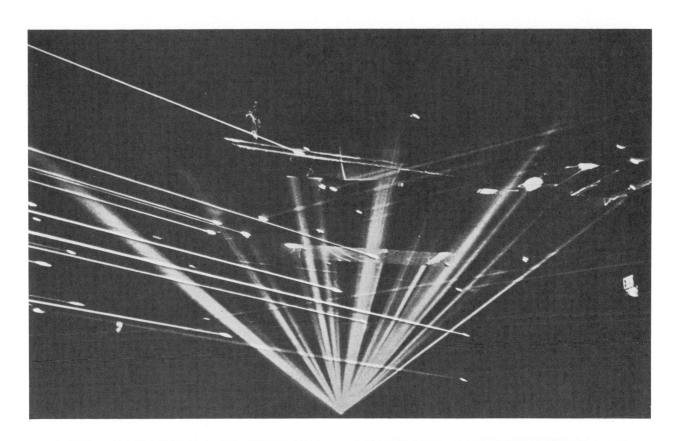

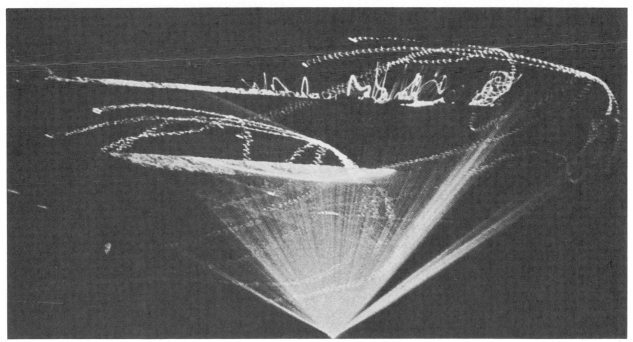

Soleil Laser Music Spectacle. Red, blue and green laser beams sweep just above the audience creating textured, three-dimensional forms in the air. (Courtesy Soleil Co.)

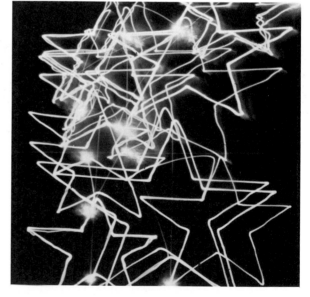

July 4, 1976 was the highlight of Soleil's Bicentennial year. Five high-power lasers were mounted at the top of the Washington Monument. After the fireworks display Soleil manned two lasers to present a specially prepared program of laser writing and five-sided stars for an estimated audience of four million people. (Courtesy Soleil Co.)

OPTICAL TRANSFORMS

Introduction

Until recently, diffraction of light has been regarded as a subject of interest only to the physicist. It is realized now, however, that the use of optical-diffraction patterns or *optical transforms*, as they have been referred to over the years, had important applications in such diverse fields as X-ray crystallography, solid state physics, optical data-processing, image enhancement, pattern recognition (such as machines for sorting mail), information storage and holography. In this section of the book we shall deal with the production of optical transforms and their application as a creative tool for artists and designers.

Transformation means the act or operation of changing from a given form, appearance or expression to another such form, appearance or expression, which in substance is equivalent. We shall see how the configuration of a diffracting aperture changes to the configuration of the diffraction pattern (transform) caused by the aperture when illuminated with laser light. It is hoped the presentation of many light diffraction patterns will stimulate thought and develop an intuitive feeling by the artists and designers about the relationship between an optical aperture and its optical transform. This is the reason for presenting here the large number of transforms for leisurly study by the reader.

The apparatus required for producing optical transforms, as described here, was kept as simple and inexpensive as possible. Description of the apparatus and procedures for making diffracting apertures and photographing the transforms follows.

The Optical Setup

When an aperture is placed within the cross section of a laser beam and the transmitted light is observed on a screen, the resulting distribution of light is called a diffraction pattern (transform).

A transparency, *A*, and a simple lens, *L*, of reasonable quality are set up as shown in the diagram. The term *transparency* can be used interchangeably with *diffraction mask*, or *diffraction aperture*, or *object*, since all objects (e.g., slits, pinholes, gratings, simple and complex graphic designs) will be black-and-white patterns recorded on 35-mm film. Different film negatives will be placed at *A* and the optical transform observed on the screen. With this setup, and a single-lens reflex camera with the lens removed, the transforms can be photographed. The camera is placed so that its film plane coincides with the focal plane of the transform lens, *L*. All photographs shown in this section were produced with this arrangement.

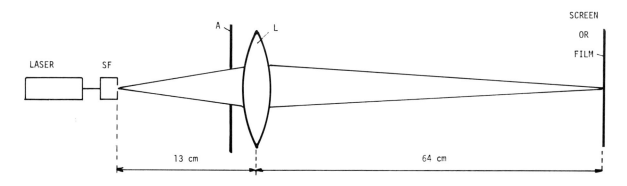

Apparatus for obtaining optical transforms

A 0.8 mW He-Ne laser (such as Metrologic ML-669) was the light source. A short focus lens converged the raw laser beam onto a pinhole to remove optical 'noise' generated by dust or dirt on the output mirror of the laser. This noise, the result of scattered light, would reduce image quality in the transform if allowed to remain. The pinhole is adjustable in two axes and the lens in the third axis. This so-called *spatial filter* (SF) produces a clean, diverging output beam to illuminate the diffracting aperture. The transform lens, *L*, was a ten-diopter (10-cm focal length) biconvex lens obtained from Edmund Scientific Co. (Barrington, NJ 08007). This lens was adjusted to form the image of the pinhole on the film (or screen). The diffracting apertures (negative film frames) were inserted into the light beam at *A*. The distance between *A* and *L* was kept at a minimum to avoid vignetting. With the given setup the diffracting apertures must be reduced on the negative film to occupy a 2-4 millimeter square area.

The first experiments should be made with black-and-white patterns obtainable from Edmund Scientific Co. Some suggested diffraction apertures are: single slit, double slit, Ronchi ruling, two Ronchi rulings crossed at 45 and 90 degrees, diffraction gratings, straight edge (a razor blade), wire or pin, circular apertures, square apertures, and rectangular apertures (IBM punchcards).

Preparation of Diffraction Apertures

Diffraction with visible laser light produces beautiful patterns with great aesthetic appeal. Any sort of an aperture will produce a diffraction pattern, but good sharply defined patterns need precision apertures. Good apertures can be made by preparing a black-on-white master design of convenient size, then photographically reducing its size and using the film negative itself as the diffracting aperture.

The aperture master can be drawn in ink on white drawing paper but ink bleeds somewhat and the resulting softly defined contours destroy the higher diffraction orders. Much better results can be obtained with press-type dry-transfer sheets obtainable in art supply stores. A large variety of lines, circles, squares, rectangles and texture screens are produced by the various manufacturers (Artype, Prestype, Formatt, Letraset, Visi-Graphics, Chartpak, Normatype, etc.). The black tape made by Chartpak (#352) is a 0.9-mm self-adhesive tape, excellent for making single, double and multiple slit masters. Diffraction gratings can be produced by photographic reduction of parallel-line screens. Cubic, rhombic and other crystal structures may be simulated by copying appropriate two-dimensional patterns. Tapestries, wallpapers and snowflake patterns are just a few additional ideas for use as aperture masters. To save film, 4 or 6 small aperture designs can be pasted up on one sheet of letter-size white paper and reduce them together to proper size on one frame of 35-mm film.

A 35-mm single-lens reflex is the most suitable camera for this work. The author used the standard lens and also a 24-mm wide-angle lens. It is important to remember that the master designs are to be reduced so that each individual aperture occupies no more than 2-4 millimeter square area on the film.

The aperture masters are illuminated evenly by placing two #1 photofloods at an angle of 45 degrees to the lens axis as shown in the diagram.

Reflector type bulbs (#1 photofloods) give good results. The center of each bulb should be about 70 cm (28 inches) from the center of the copyboard. Use a lens shade. To minimize flare, the lens must be absolutely clean. For greatest sharpness the image must be carefully focused and the camera and copyboard must be on solid support. The shutter should be tripped with a cable release and room illumination turned off during exposure. The author used Kodak High Contrast Copy Film, Type 5069 to photograph the aperture masks. This film is widely available in camera stores preloaded in 35-exposure cartridges.

A reflected-light exposure reading should be taken based on a tungsten rating of ASA 64. The exposure time used was always 1/15th second. If no light meter is available trial exposures should be made at f/11, f/8 and f/5.6.

The exposed film was developed in Kodak D-19 for six minutes at 20°C (68°F) with agitation at 30 second intervals. Manufacturer's instructions were followed for rinse, stop bath, fixing and washing. A one-minute rinse in Kodak Photo-Flo Solution after final washing is recommended to minimize drying marks. Drying must be done in dust free room. The developed film is cut and each frame is mounted in cardboard or glassless diabinders, such as made by "gepe". The negatives must not be mounted between cover glasses.

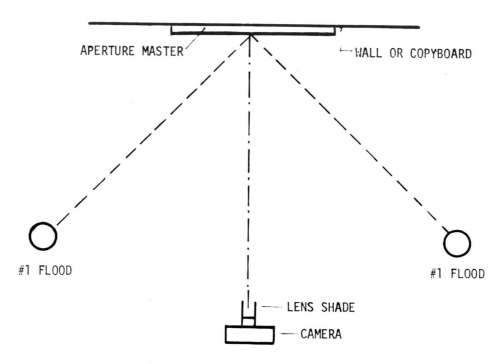

Photographing the aperture master

Photographing the Optical Transforms

The 35-mm single-lens reflex camera with the lens removed took the place of the observation screen. Kodak Panatomic-X film was used. Exposure times ranged from 1/8th to 1/60th second. Kodak Microdol-X or D-76 developers each gave good results and processing was according to manufacturer's instructions. Prints were made on Kodak Polycontrast Rapid II RC glossy paper.

As a starting point, the biconvex lens, *L*, is about 13 cm from the pinhole of the spatial filter and the film plane of the camera approximately 64 cm from the lens. Focusing is done through the reflex finder either by moving the camera or by moving the lens until the transform seen on the groundglass is sharp. Using the recommended low-power laser, or any other laser with between 0.5 to 1.0 mW output, when the diffracting aperture is in place, there is no danger to the eye while focusing. To avoid eye fatigue while making a large number of exposures, wear dark sunglasses.

Some Properties of Optical Transforms

A general study of optical transforms shows that:
a) Diffraction detail is reciprocal to aperture detail: the larger the aperture, the smaller the diffraction pattern, and vice versa.
b) If two similar apertures are placed parallel to each other, the diffraction pattern is the same as that of each separately, crossed by (Young's) fringes; the fringes are perpendicular to the separation of the apertures, and the larger the separation of the two apertures the finer fringe spacings they produce.
c) All transforms have a center of symmetry even when the aperture itself has no apparent symmetry.
d) An aperture which is symmetric about an axis will generate a transform which is symmetric about two lines, one parallel and one perpendicular to that axis. As an example, a triangle has three lines of symmetry and consequently its transform has six such axis.
e) The transform does not change as the aperture is moved in its own plane provided, of course, that the whole aperture remains within the cross-section of the laser beam.
f) Rotation of the aperture produces rotation of the transform. The transform always rotates about a parallel axis passing through the symmetry center of the transform. Both aperture and transform rotate with the same angular speed.
g) The transform of a complicated aperture may be regarded as the sum of the transforms of a few simple units into which the complex aperture can be broken down.

The Plates

The illustrative material is organized as follows: On the left-hand pages there are four drawings representing four diffracting apertures. The corresponding transform photos are on the right-hand pages. Thus, for example, the upper left photo shows the transform resulting from the upper left diffracting aperture.

 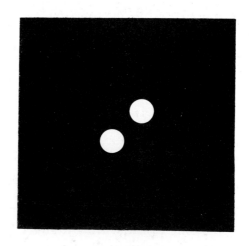

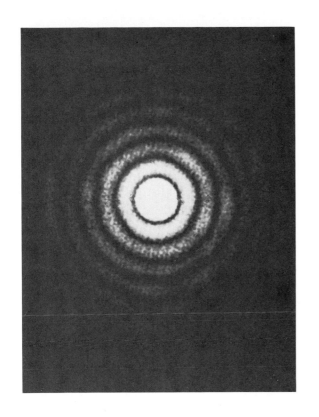

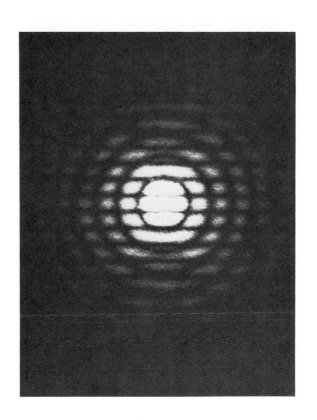

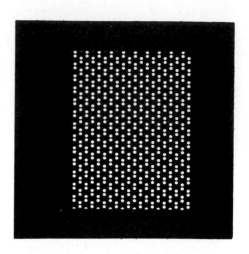

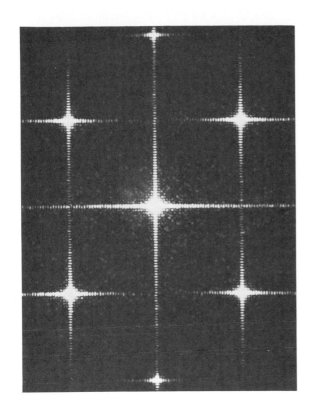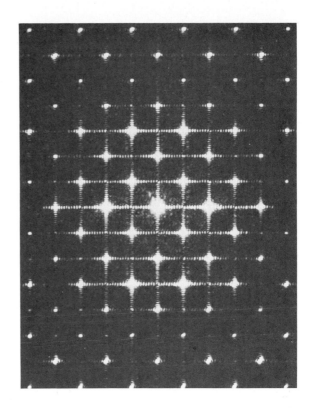

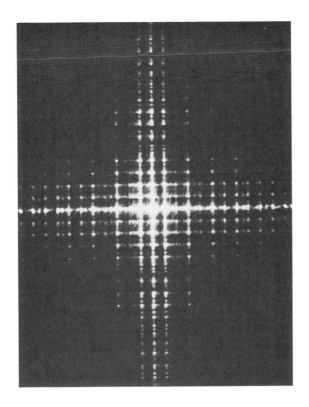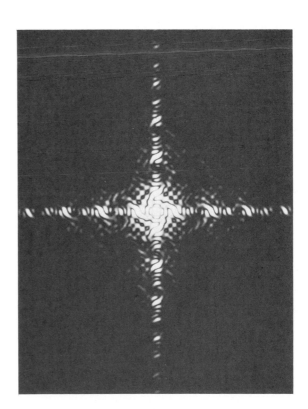

 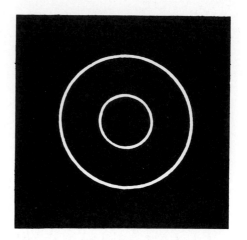

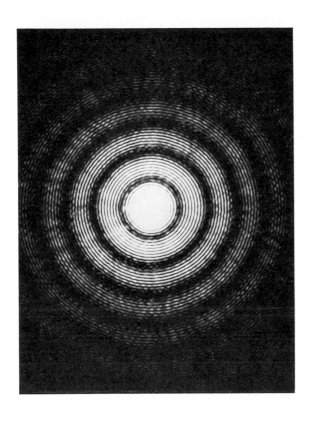

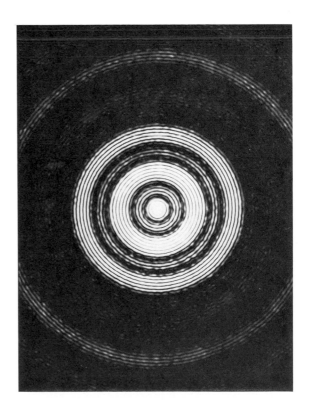

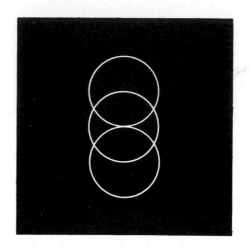

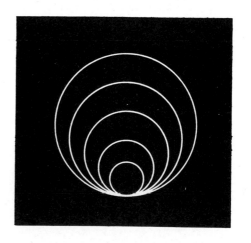

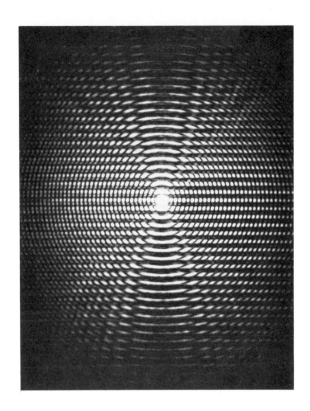

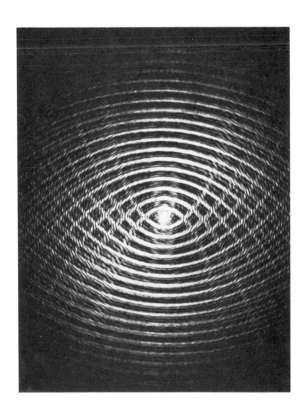

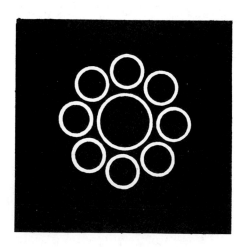

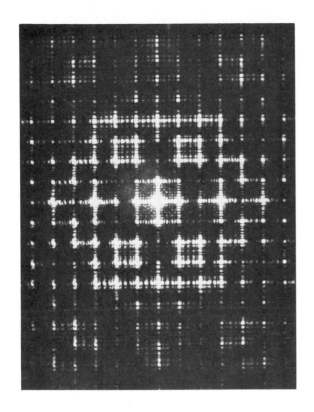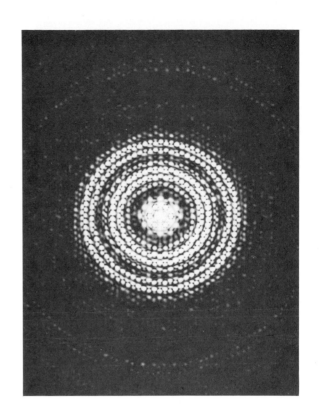

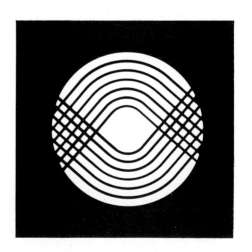

 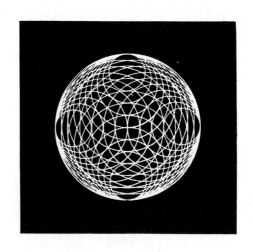

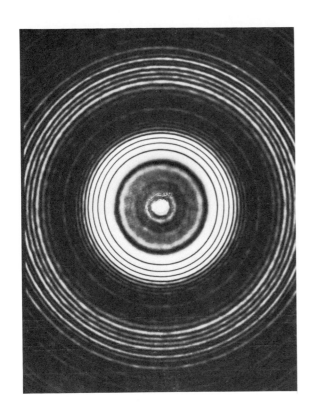

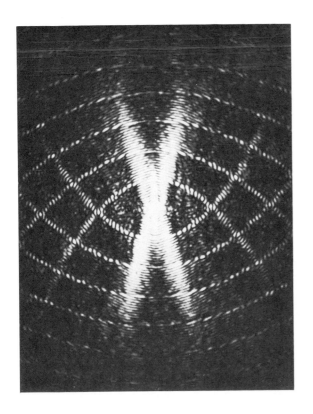

 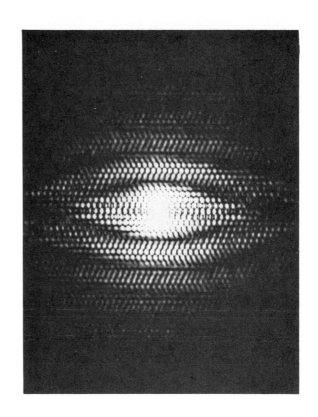

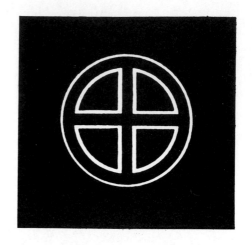

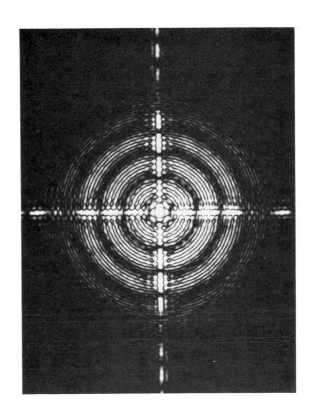

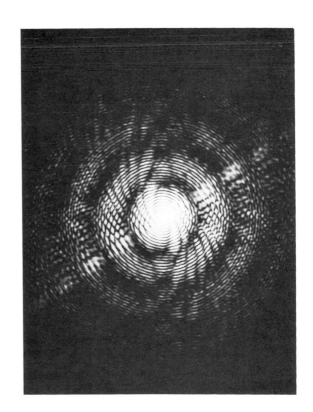
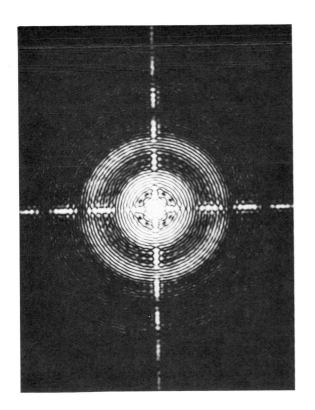

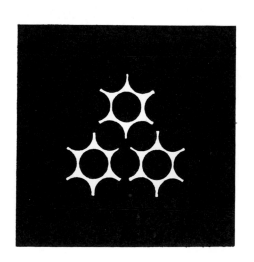

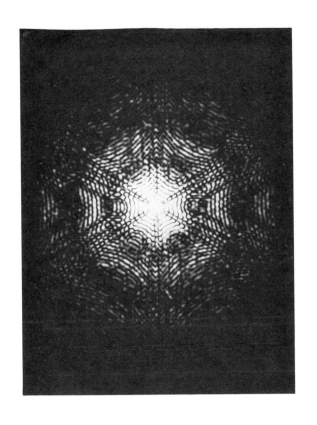

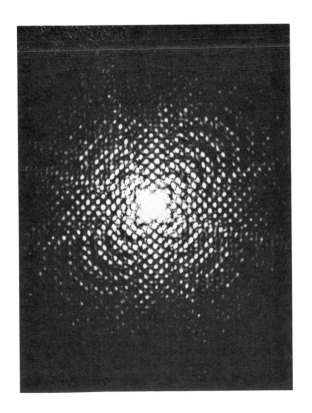

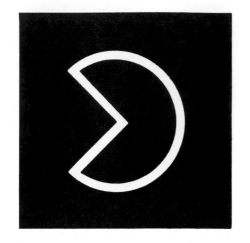 

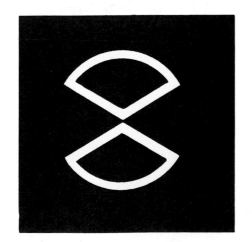 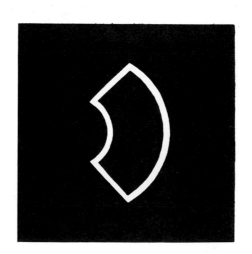

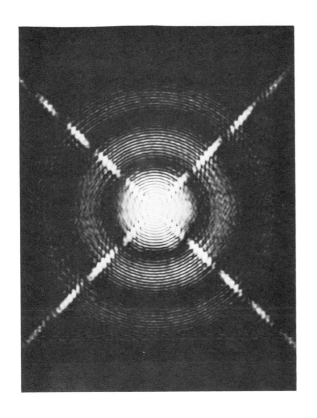 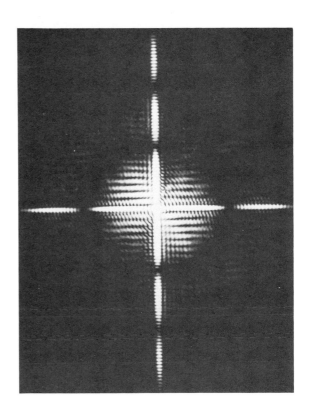

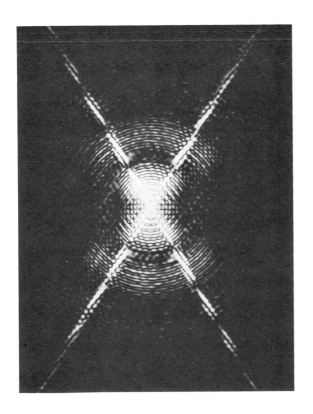 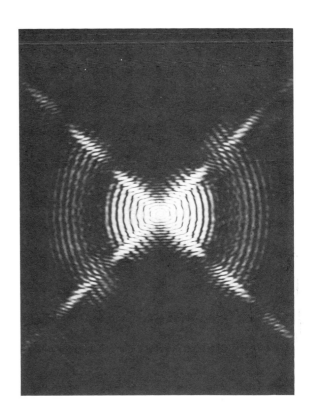

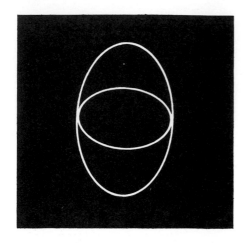

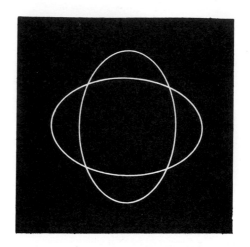

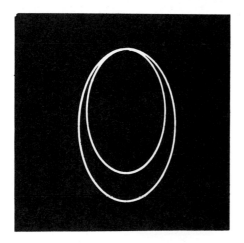

80

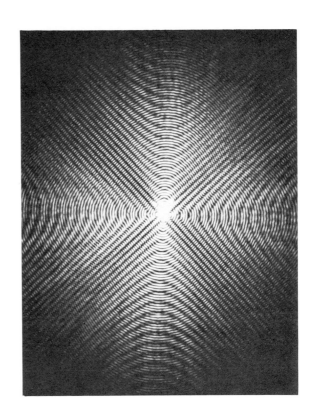

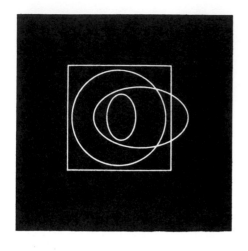

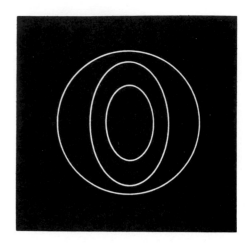

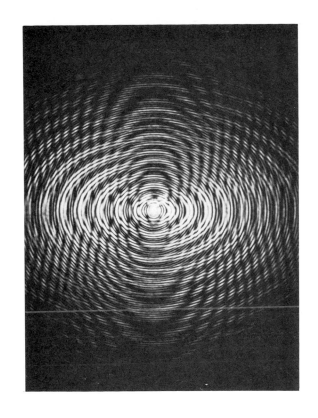

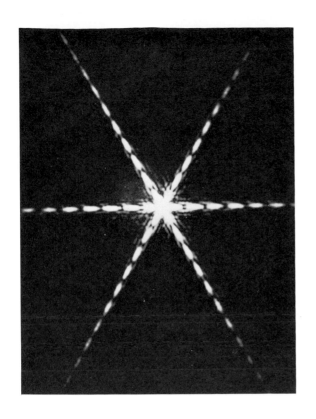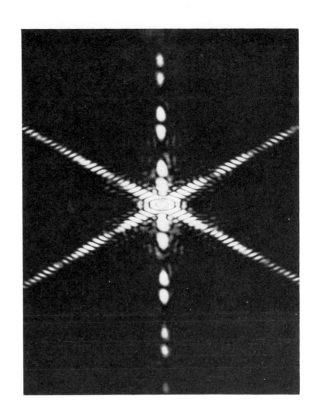

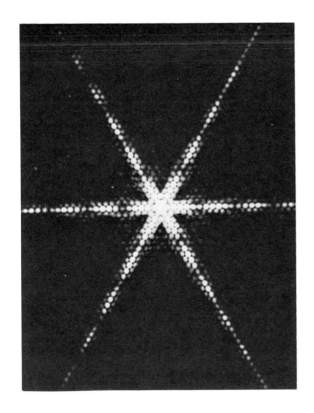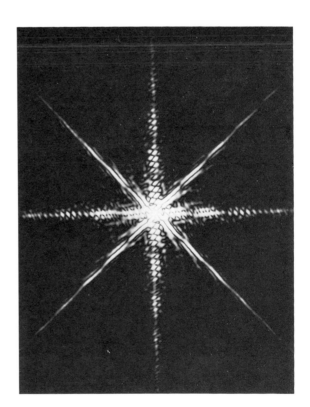

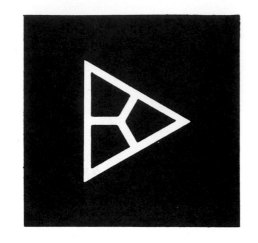

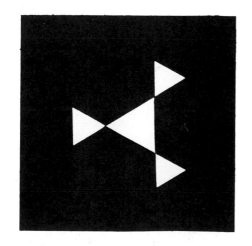

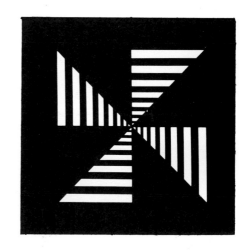

86

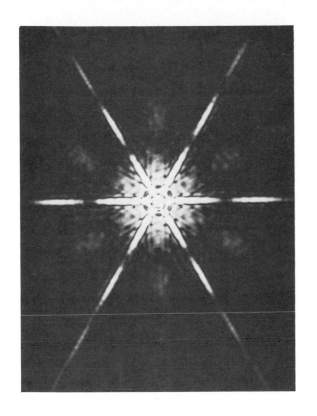 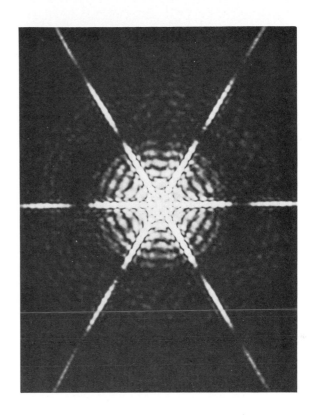

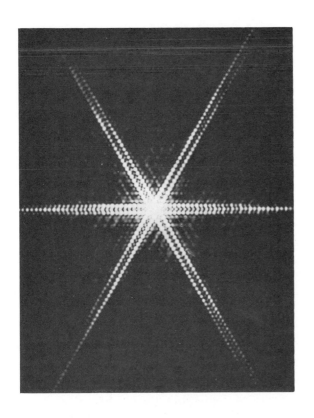 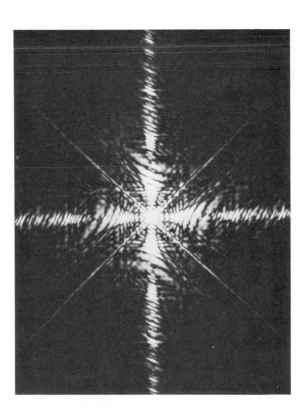

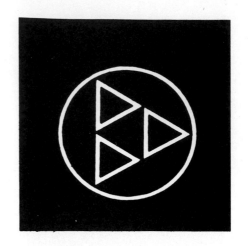

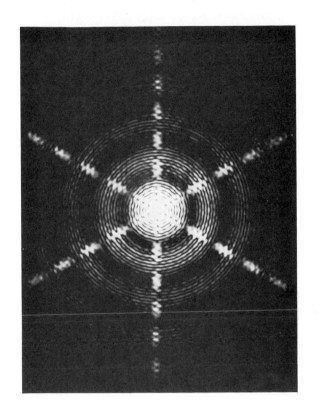 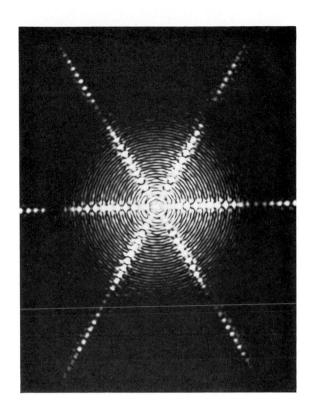

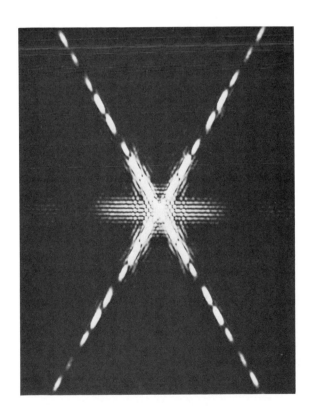 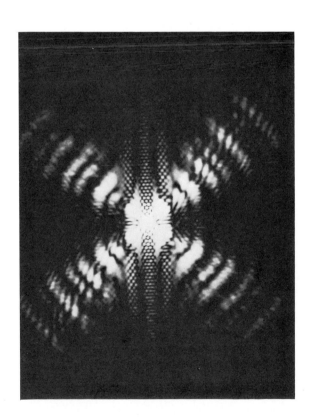

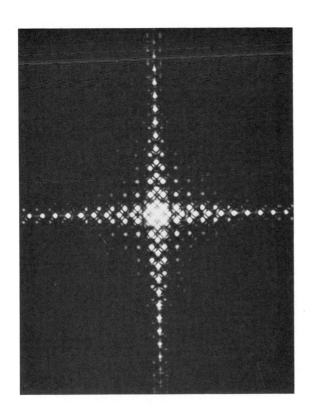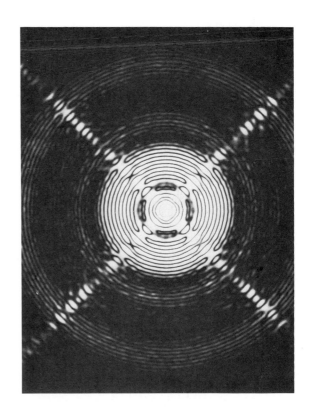

92

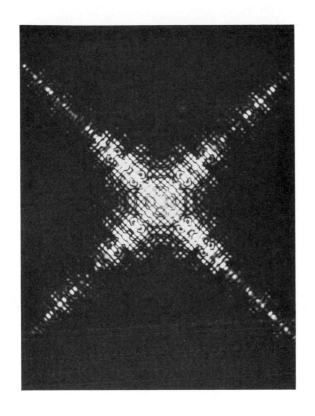

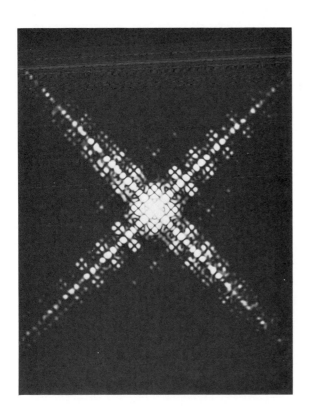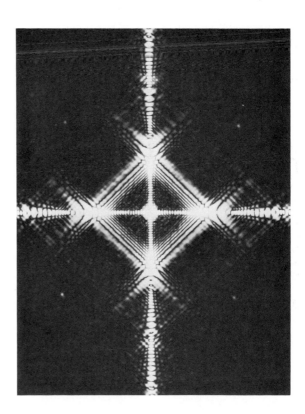

 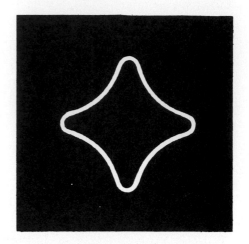

94

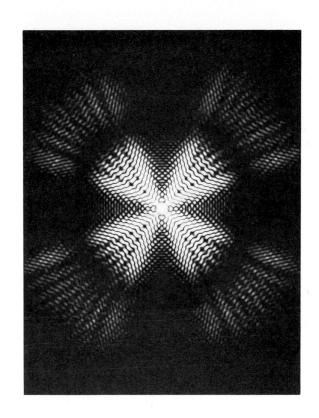

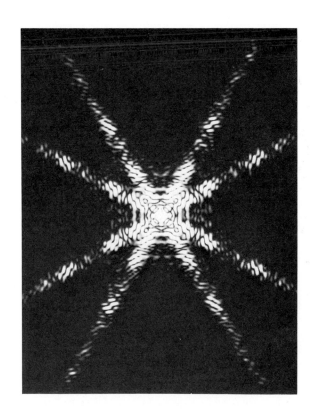

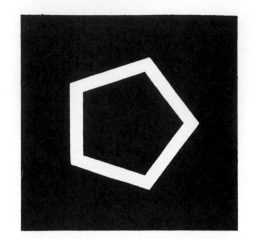

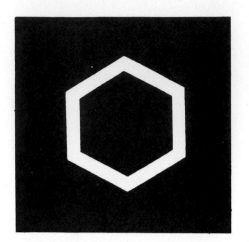

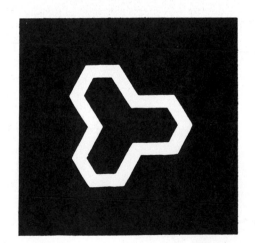

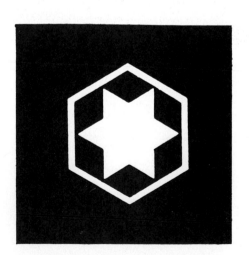

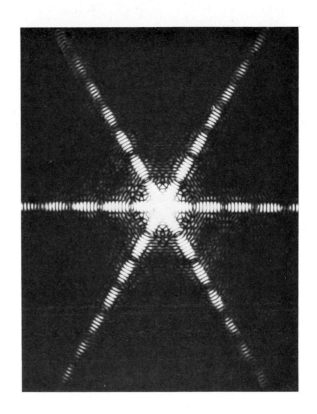

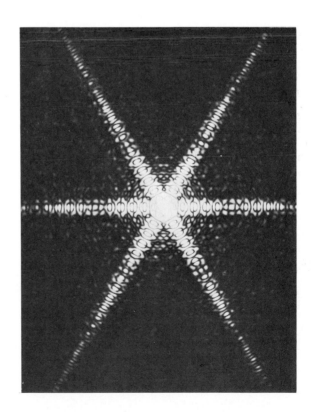

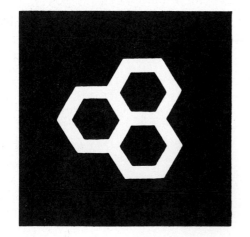

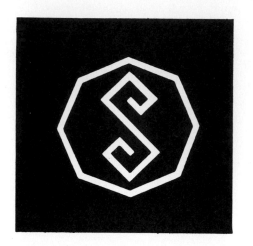

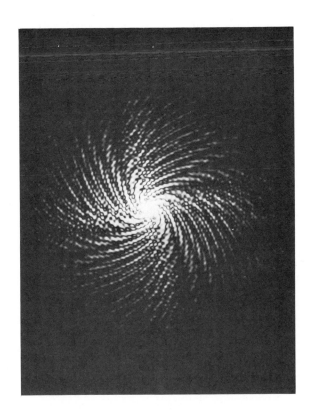

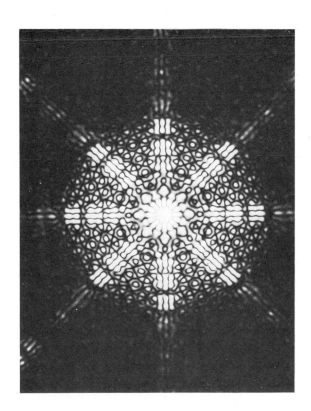

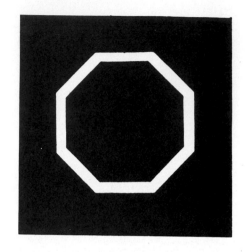

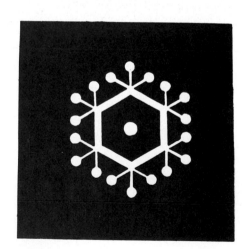

114

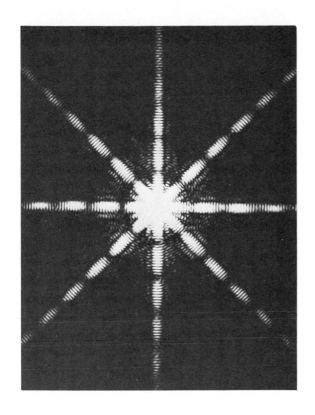 

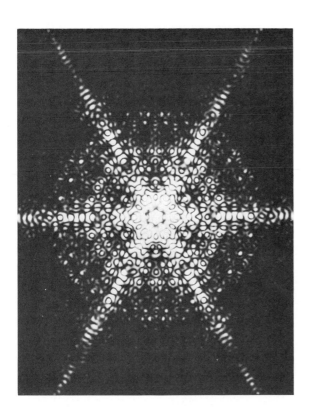 

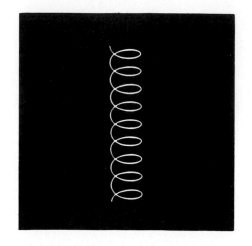 

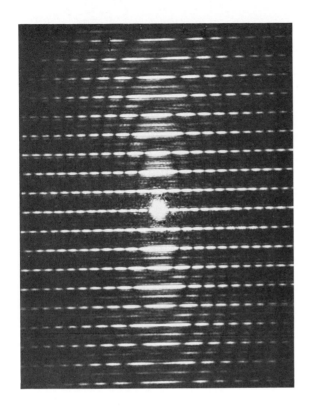

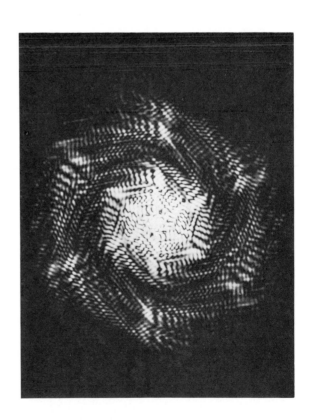

HOLOGRAPHY

When looking at a hologram for the first time, most people react with astonishment; sometimes with disbelief. They see, first, an almost clear plate of glass. Then, as they look into the illuminated holographic display, a three-dimensional scene appears on the other side of the plate. It looks like a real scene but, when they reach around the plate to touch the objects, their fingers pass right through the image. It comes as a shock to discover that the imagery exists only in the form of light. Baffled, the viewers wonder how it is possible to see something that really is not there. And how it is possible that the image is three-dimensional. The viewers become even more fascinated when they move about a bit and the perspective in the imagery changes. They notice the parallax between the near and far objects and by changing position they can see what lies behind an obstructing object. And when they shift attention from a near object to a far one it becomes necessary to refocus the eyes. Can this be explained as an optical illusion? It certainly cannot because if the viewer has a camera and attempts to take a picture of what is observed, the camera has to be focused on either the near or the far object, or the camera lens has to be stopped down to achieve the necessary depth of focus.

Conventional photography, which has been with us for well over a century, provides a flat, two-dimensional representation of the scene being recorded. A stereoscopic photograph is not truly three-dimensional because it captures the scene from one angle only and it is not possible to look around an object in the picture by moving one's head. With photography we record only the intensity distribution across a light beam — all the phase information is lost. The loss of phase information results in the loss of one dimension.

Holography provides a method of recording the missing phase information by using a reference beam of light with which to compare the phase of the light scattered and reflected from the object (scene) to be recorded. The interaction of the light scattered from the object and the reference beam produces an interference pattern which is stationary in position and which is recorded on a photographic plate. After development, the plate is referred to as a *hologram*, from the Greek word *holos* which means "the whole," because it contains the whole of the information about the objects in the scene. The technique of recording holograms is called *holography* and because holography is an interference technique, the recording light must be coherent in space and time. Laser light has these qualities.

Holography is a two-step process of optical imagery. During the recording process, the single beam of laser light is split into two components. One component is directed to a recording medium, usually an ultra-high resolution photographic emulsion, and is called the *reference wave*. The other component is aimed at the object or scene to be recorded. This second component is scattered from the object and this complex wave which is called the *object wave* is now allowed to fall on the recording medium. Since both the reference and object waves come from the same source, they are mutually coherent. As they meet in the plane of the recording medium they form a stable interference pattern. This interference pattern is a complex system of microscopic fringes. It can be seen, thus, that the intensity and the relative phase of the light coming from the object is stored, after exposure and development, on the photographic emulsion in a kind of optical code.

The second step in holography is the re-creation of an intelligible image from the hologram. Holograms cannot be decoded at sight. They must be illuminated with a laser beam which is similar to the original reference beam used to record the hologram. The *playback* laser beam is transmitted through the millions of fringes on the hologram resulting in a complex diffracted wave. Local variations in the contrast and spacing of the fringes produce local variations in the amplitude and direction of the diffracted playback beam. When the hologram is properly illuminated, the result is an undeviated wave and first-order diffracted waves on each side. One of the first-order waves exactly duplicates the original object wave. By viewing this *reconstructed wavefront*, one sees an image which appears as though the original object(s) were in place and includes three-dimensional effects with parallax.

During the past fifteen years a number of hologram-making and hologram-viewing systems have been developed. The two broad categories of holograms are: *Transmission holograms* which are viewed by passing light through them toward the viewer, and *reflection holograms*, those viewed by directing light on them from the front.

For those readers who are not familiar with holograms, a large selection of both types is available commercially and they are not expensive. Write to the Museum of Holography Bookstore, 11 Mercer Street, New York, NY 10013 and to Edmund Scientific Co., Barrington, NJ 08007 and ask for their mail-order catalogs.

* * *

To make a **transmission hologram** of a solid 3-D object, an arrangement like the one shown in the illustration may be used.

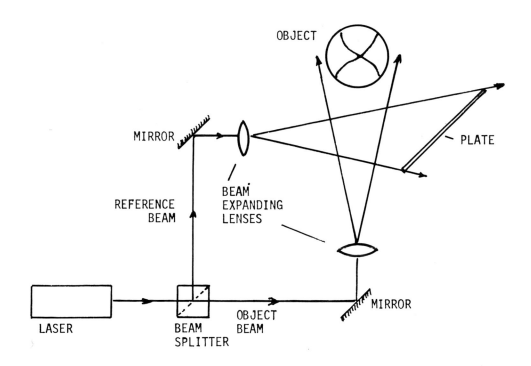

Arrangement for recording transmission holograms

With a beam splitter the laser beam is split into two and both beams are spread out by lenses. One expanding beam, the reference beam, falls directly on the photographic plate. The other expanding beam, the object beam, illuminates the object. The light scattered from the object and the reference beam overlap to produce an interference pattern which is recorded on the plate. Special, ultra-high resolution emulsions are required to record the microscopic interference patterns. The plate is then processed like an ordinary photographic plate or film and, after development, is referred to as the *hologram.*

The reconstruction, or viewing stage of holography is essentially a retracing of the hologram-forming stage. To view the hologram (see drawing) the processed plate is illuminated with the reference beam. During the recording process the reference beam acts as a kind of coder; during reconstruction the hologram is decoded by the same reference beam.

The interference pattern recorded on the emulsion diffracts some of the incident light into a wave field similar to the wave field that would have existed in space, had the photographic plate not intercepted the scattered light from the object. The observer gets the impression of looking through a window (the hologram) at the original object.

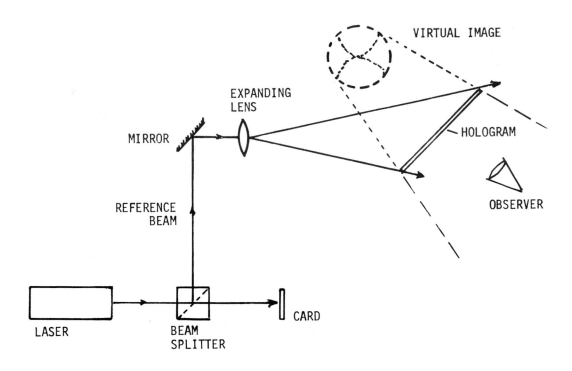

Arrangement for viewing a transmission hologram

Of course, to reproduce a faithful 3-D image of the original object it is not necessary to replace the hologram in the original recording configuration as indicated in the drawing. All that is necessary is to illuminate the hologram with a diverging laser beam similar to the reference beam originally used in constructing the hologram. It is, however, very instructive to replace the developed plate in its original position. If this is done, the holographic reconstruction and the original object can be compared directly. If the reference beam is blocked with a card, one can see the illuminated original object through the semi-transparent hologram. If the card is then used to block the object beam, then the reconstruction can be observed. The holographic image cannot be distinguished from the real one. The reconstruction shows horizontal and vertical parallax.

* * *

It is possible to produce holograms which do not require a laser for viewing. With this technique the reconstructed wave fields are obtained by reflection from the hologram rather than transmission through it. To record a

white light reflection hologram, the photographic plate is illuminated from both sides, that is, the object wave illuminates one side of the emulsion while the reference beam exposes it from the opposite side. Thus, the object wave and the reference beam are traveling through the emulsion in opposite directions. Standing waves are set up in depth in the emulsion and the interference patterns are in the form of planes essentially parallel to the plane of the emulsion. Upon processing, each layer of silver grains, when illuminated with white light, acts as a mirror. Some of the light is reflected, the remainder passes through the emulsion or is partially absorbed. The back of the plate is often coated with black to provide a dark background for the reconstruction. The drawing shows the optical setup used to record and view reflection holograms.

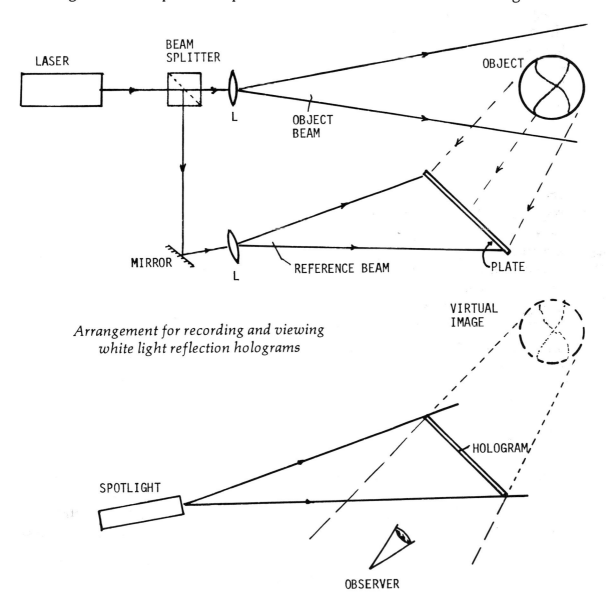

Arrangement for recording and viewing white light reflection holograms

The laser beam spread by an expanding lens is made to illuminate the object. The scattered light from the object illuminates one side of the photographic plate. A portion of the laser beam is diverted to a steering mirror by the beam splitter, and then this reference beam is spread by a lens so that it covers the other side of the photographic plate. Naturally, the photographic plate used with this technique must not have an anti-halation backing.

When processed, the hologram can be viewed by white light, sunlight, flashlight, spotlight, slide projector or with an unfrosted electric light bulb. The hologram is tilted until the illumination striking the plate is at the same angle as did the reference beam during the recording. If the hologram was recorded with a red (He-Ne) gas laser one would expect the reconstructed image to be red in color. This is not so, because, in practice, the emulsion shrinks during processing and the interference effects among the reflecting layers yield a greenish image. If, after processing, the emulsion is re-swelled, the reflection hologram will reconstruct in the color of the recording laser light. Reflection holograms, like transmission holograms show both horizontal and vertical parallax.

* * *

Phase holograms. A conventional hologram has very low *diffraction efficiency* (ratio of incident to usable diffracted light in the viewing process). While transmission holograms recorded on a high-resolution silver halide emulsion show a maximum efficiency of about 6%, these emulsions may be *bleached* to form a *phase hologram.* Due to the absence of attenuation, phase holograms may achieve efficiencies between 30% to 45%. Reflection holograms also may be bleached and, at least theoretically, the efficiency can approach 100%.

The bleaching process dissolves the metallic silver from the emulsion so that no density remains and the imagewise thickness variations of the emulsion result in the desired phase modulation of the playback light. Other bleaching processes change the metallic silver into transparent compounds having a refractive index higher than that of the surrounding medium. These imagewise index variations impose the desired phase modulation onto the playback illumination.

Phase holograms may be produced by contact printing or direct recording onto a *photoresist* material. They may also be produced by using a *thermoplastic* material as the recording medium. Phase holograms formed in *dichromated gelatin* film are the sharpest and brightest holograms currently produced. Dichromate holograms are sealed in glass to protect the gelatin from moisture.

* * *

Pulsed laser transmission holograms. Through the development of short-pulse ruby lasers with both high energy and high coherence, it has become quite simple to make short-exposure holograms of rather large objects. One consequence of this development is that holography is no longer a science for which an interferometrically stable laboratory environment is absolutely necessary.

With the use of Q-switched ruby lasers stability of the optical apparatus ceases to be a problem and holograms of rapidly moving objects can be recorded in the same way an electronic flash is used in photography. The ruby wavelength (694.3 nm) is quite close to the He-Ne wavelength (632.8 nm) and, therefore, a continuous-wave He-Ne laser can be used for playback of the pulsed holograms. The holographic arrangement is the same as depicted earlier for the recording of transmission holograms.

Pulsed holography is used for non-destructive materials testing, flight ballistics analyses, detonation and flame propagation studies, vibration analysis, and medical diagnostics. To an artist, pulsed laser portraits of human subjects and action holograms of dancers are very exciting.

Pulsed laser holography has important applications in the preservation and restoration of statuary. Pulsed laser holograms of art treasures reproduce reality perfectly and, thus, have great archival utility. One can envision holographic museums which will provide a visual record of art treasures from all over the world. Also, holographic records might serve as templates in repairing damaged museum pieces. Holograms are expected to become important visual aids in teaching art history and techniques. It is important to note that the holographic image can be analyzed in much the same way as the original object. Thus, it can be viewed either in totality, or a particular spot can be examined with a microscope!

* * *

Rainbow holograms. Holographic information content far exceeds requirements for viewing pleasing three-dimensional images. Human binocular vision is horizontally oriented. Vertical perspectives can be sacrificed with little loss. The rainbow hologram, invented by Dr. Stephen A. Benton, takes advantage of the horizontal geometry of the human visual system. His method involves two steps. First, a conventional transmission hologram is recorded. This, primary hologram, is masked off except for a narrow horizontal aperture. Primary information reduction is achieved by using the narrow aperture. For example, using a 1 mm high aperture with a 100 mm high hologram reduces vertical information content 100:1. The aperture width should be at least equal to normal interocular spacing but, preferably, should be wider.

The second step is to record a second hologram in a plane near the position of the image produced by the properly illuminated primary hologram. The drawing illustrates the method for producing the secondary (rainbow) hologram.

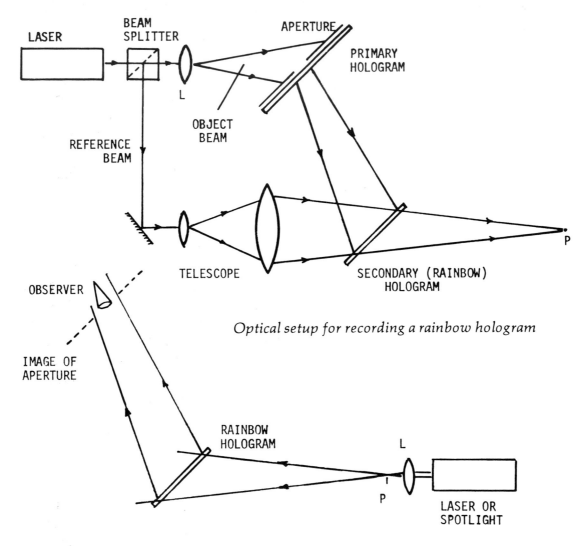

Optical setup for recording a rainbow hologram

Arrangement for viewing a rainbow hologram

The laser beam is divided by the beamsplitter into two components. One component illuminates the masked off primary hologram which is tilted so that a real image of the original object is produced. A second photographic plate is placed near the space occupied by the real image. A telescope increases the cross section of the second component (the reference beam) and also focuses the beam at *P*. The two wave fields interfere and the secondary (Benton, or "rainbow") hologram is produced. The Benton hologram records a holographic image of the illuminated aperture as well as the information limited real image of the object. It is viewed by properly illuminating it with a laser to form a real image of the aperture. Realistic stereoscopic images of the original object are viewed by looking through the aperture image as if it were a window. If the observer moves his head vertically the image disappears. If the laser is replaced with white light illumination, the image of the aperture is vertically smeared into a continuous spectrum. As the observer moves his head vertically the image changes color but remains clear and sharp. If the observer places his eyes in a plane other than the plane in which the image of the aperture is formed, the color will change from top to bottom. Because of this prismatic effect, these holograms are often called rainbow holograms.

The latest development is a one-step method for recording rainbow holograms. Invented by H. Chen and F. T. S. Yu, the technique simplifies the somewhat cumbersome and expensive two-step recording process. The diagram shows the recording geometry for this new method which eliminates the need for the primary hologram.

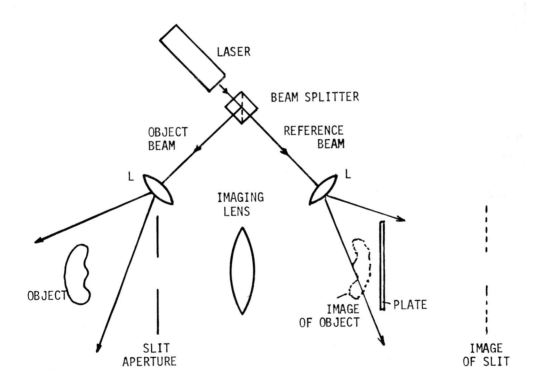

One-step method for recording rainbow holograms

An imaging lens and a narrow slit are inserted between the recording plate and the object. A real image of the object is formed at the front of the photographic plate, and a real image of the slit is formed behind the plate. The disadvantage of the method is that the use of an imaging lens restricts the field of view due to vignetting. A method introduced by P. N. Tamura helps to overcome this disadvantage: two lenses are used in the method. The imaging lens covered by a horizontal slit takes the image of the object. A second lens, a field lens, is placed in the image plane immediately in front of the photographic plate. The field lens forms the image of the slit behind the plate; it acts as a field lens for the object beam and as a collimator for the reference beam. The maximum size of the image is limited by the size of the field lens. Rainbow holograms show either horizontal or vertical parallax but not both at the same time.

* * *

Kinetic holograms.

Integral photography is the name given to Lippmann's technique (1908) of multi-stereo photography. In integral photography, an array of tiny lenses, either lenticular or fly's-eye, is used to form multiple, spatially distinct images of a scene at the back focal plane of the array. Each image is complete, as seen by a particular lenslet in the array. For playback, a positive transparency is repositioned at the focal plane of the lens array and illuminated by diffuse light from the transparency side. The image is then seen at the original location of the object. The great advantage of integral photography is that it does not involve interference. Thus, there are no limitations as to subject matter, also, light and stability requirements are the same as those for ordinary photography.

The great disadvantages of integral photography are: 1) It requires very careful registration of the transparency with the fly's-eye lens array, 2) it produces a screen effect due to the lenslets, and 3) the image is depth-inverted (pseudoscopic). In 1967, R. V. Pole overcame these limitations by using laser light for playback and recording a hologram. The problem of depth-inversion was thus solved, since the real image of a hologram is pseudoscopic and a doubly pseudoscopic image is orthoscopic. Somewhat later, D. J. De Bitetto developed an approach to *holographic movies.* De Bitetto knew that vertical parallax is seldom of value due to human binocular vision and, therefore, eliminated it from his system. De Bitetto demonstrated that a series of strip holograms can be moved in front of an observer to produce a series of images with good horizontal parallax. He used a series of ordinary photographs of 3-D objects taken on ordinary reversal film. The processed 2-D positive transparencies were sequentially illuminated with laser light and projected on a translucent screen. The holographic plate was then exposed through a movable aperture mask which was positioned immediately in front of the plate. The usual reference beam was also directed onto the plate through the aperture mask and one strip was recorded for each 2-D transparency. Aperture width was carefully chosen to avoid both loss of resolution and jumps in the image as the viewer moved in front of the composite hologram.

The current holographic movie making process combines cinematography and holography. It must be pointed out that, at present, holographic movies run for about 45 seconds and only a few people can observe them at the same time.

Over the last six years the so-called **white light integral (multiplex) holography** technique was perfected by physicist Lloyd G. Cross, and his colleagues at the Multiplex Company in San Francisco. In recent years, Hart Perry, Jr., the 1977 Academy Award winning cinematographer of the documentary, "Harlan County, USA," established The Holographic Film Company, Inc. in New York City for the purpose of exploring multiplex holography as an advertising tool and a means of artistic expression.

The most important advantage of white light multiplex holograms is their capability to record holographically any subject, large or small, indoors or outdoors. There is no need for laser light illumination in the recording stage of multiplex holograms and, for playback, a clear-glass single-filament light bulb is used to illuminate the composite hologram. Limited subject motion is permissible and is perceived either by having the viewer walk about the hologram or by rotating the hologram itself in front of a stationary observer.

The multiplex technique involves the use of a movie camera to take hundreds of pictures of a subject placed on a slowly rotating turntable. Conventional studio spots and flood lights are used for illumination. Cross uses a standard 35-mm Mitchell cine camera loaded with Kodak Plus-X negative film and the camera is operated at 24 frames per second. Since the turntable makes one full revolution in 45 seconds, 1080 frames are exposed for a 360-degree hologram. Perry uses 16-mm movie cameras, such as Bolex or Arriflex, and his preferred film is Kodak 7276 Plus-X Reversal. While a rotating platform is used routinely in the studio, dancers leaping and turning have also been filmed without a turntable, and the Statue of Liberty has been filmed from a circling helicopter.

The exposed movie film is processed and then a narrow strip hologram is made from each movie frame. This is done with a special optical printer designed and built by Cross (see simplified diagram).

A movie projector is used to hold the film footage. A He-Ne laser beam is split into two beams: the object beam is expanded to illuminate the film gate. A complex lens system is used to enlarge and invert the film frame. Finally, a large cylindrical lens, especially designed and constructed by Cross, com-

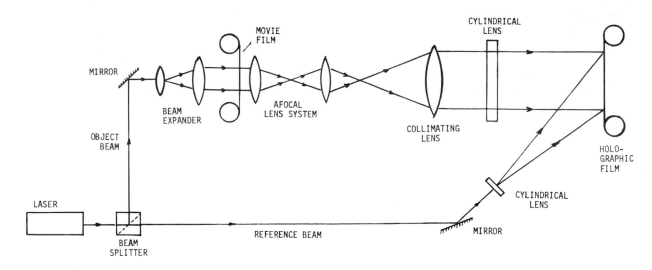

Arrangement for conversion of 2-D movie film transparencies into a composite hologram of as many contiguous vertical strip holograms

presses the image in the shape of a narrow strip and focuses it on the holographic film. The reference beam, after leaving the beam splitter, passes through another cylindrical lens which expands the beam into a strip of light to strike the holographic film at about 45-degree angle superimposed over the image carried by the object beam. After one movie frame is recorded as a strip hologram the movie film is advanced by one frame and the holographic film is advanced by the width of one strip. Then, the second film frame is converted into a strip hologram etc. until 1080 conversions are completed for a 360-degree composite hologram. After conventional processing and bleaching, the composite hologram, the final product, is mounted inside a curved or cylindrical Plexiglas display. A bare incandescent bulb is used to illuminate the hologram usually from below eye level and hidden from the viewer. As the observer views the plastic drum with the hologram mounted inside, he sees over 50 strips (movie frames) simultaneously but the images formed on the two retinas are slightly different and as a result a three-dimensional image is perceived.

In commercial displays the Plexiglas drum is slowly rotated by an electric motor. The entire unit, including the light source, is placed on a pedestal and the audience forms a circle around it to view the moving 3-D images.

* * *

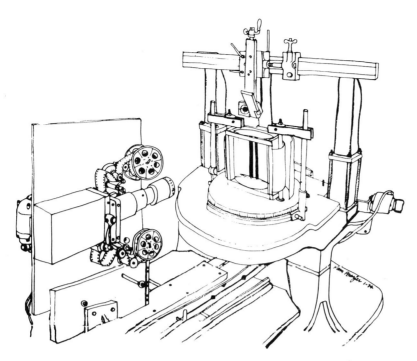

Multiplex optical printer (courtesy Multiplex Corp.)

Holography in science and industry. As has been noted, with holography one can create highly realistic three-dimensional images, both static and kinetic. But holography can do much more, like the creation of stunning, abstract imagery in space. Space can be turned inside-out via pseudoscopic imagery. Pictorial as well as sculptural effects can be achieved. When viewing a hologram one feels compelled to explore, to become a participant: we move closer, and then further away, up and then down, to one side and then the other, and delight in the visual experiences created by our own movement.

With holography we can study dynamic effects at our leisure. We can observe objects under stress. We can see sound, analyze, or just marvel at beautiful vibration patterns. There are many things we can do with holography that are possible in no other way.

Holography has been a powerful research tool for about fifteen years. The most useful holographic technique is holographic interferometry and its most effective application is vibration analysis. Holographers, practitioners of the delightful art of holography, discovered their art has not only power but beauty as well. The following photos give a small sampling.

Possibilities such as three-dimensional television and cinema for large audiences are still ahead. Both the science and art of holography are still moving forward and we can expect to find ever widening horizons.

Emmeth Leith and Juris Upatnieks. *Train and Bird*. 1964. Transmission hologram. Collection of the Museum of Holography. Copyright, Leith and Upatnieks, 1964.

Photograph of the reconstruction of a hologram of Donatello's *John the Baptist*. The hologram was recorded in Venice, Italy, the home of the statue. The photograph was made in Los Angeles, California, from a hologram which was brought back. (Courtesy R.F. Wuerker, TRW Systems Group.)

During the Spring of 1972 an experimental study was conducted in Venice, Italy, to demonstrate the feasibility of *in-situ* holography of life-sized statuary and wood-carvings. Emphasis was on subjects in a state of accelerating disintegration, the result of environmental processes. Archival image records of several Venetian art objects were produced by pulsed ruby-laser holography. The picture above is the photograph of the holographic image of the wood-carving *John the Baptist* (San Giovanni Battista) by Donatello. The laser reference beam can be seen on the left. (Courtesy R.F. Wuerker, TRW Systems Group.)

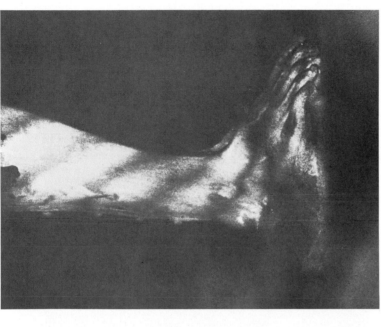

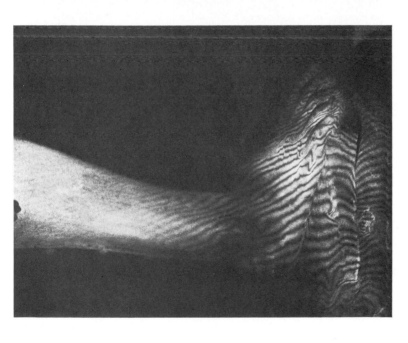

Holographic interferogram of the leg of Donatello's *John the Baptist.* The fringe pattern is the result of recording two holograms on the same photographic plate and making a change in the surface between the two exposures. In one example, the leg was warmed with an electric light bulb between the two exposures. The leg expanded. The hologram revealed the location of cracks and disbanded portions of the surface. In the other example, the change was due to a decrease in local humidity, produced by putting the statue in a plastic box with drying crystals. A time of about fifteen minutes separated the two hologram exposures. These pictures show the application of holographic non-destructive testing to the inspection of flaws in art treasures. (Courtesy R.F. Wuerker, TRW Systems Group.)

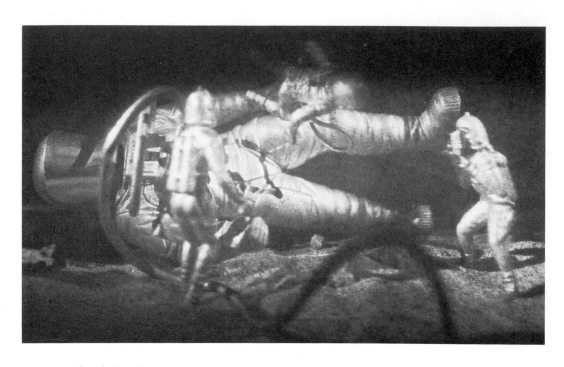

Jerry Pethic/Lloyd Cross. *Spaceman.* 1974. White light transmission hologram. Collection of the Museum of Holography. Copyright, Jerry Pethick, 1974. (photo Rosemary H. Jackson)

Stephen A. Benton. *Rind II.* 1977. White light
transmission hologram. Collection of the Museum of
Holography. Copyright, Stephen A. Benton, 1977.
(photo Brad Cantos)

Peter Nicholson. *Self-Portrait After Escher*, March, 1977. (Photo by Harvey Reed.) The Center for Experimental Holography, under the direction of Peter Nicholson, is dedicated to explore the unique 3-dimensional capabilities of holography, especially in the fields of art, portraiture and museum holography. The Center evolved out of the Smithsonian Institution's Holography Program at Brookhaven National Laboratory, and is presently involved in a joint research program with the Departments of Physics and Art at the University of Hawaii at Manoa. The Center's pulsed ruby laser system has been designed to create life-size holographic portraits as well as master holograms of rare and unique museum artifacts.

William J. Molteni. *Self-recognition*. 1977. Two views of a pulsed laser transmission hologram. Facility: The Center for Experimental Holography at Brookhaven National Laboratories. Copyright, William J. Molteni. (photo Chris Weidner)

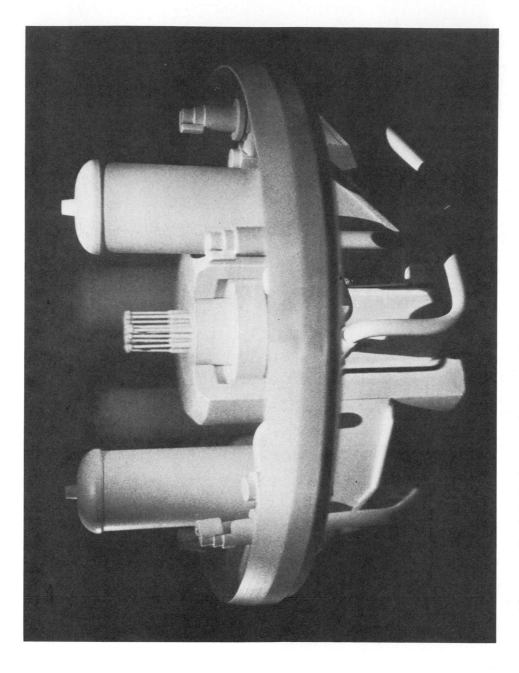

Photograph of the hologram showing *Rolls–Royce Limited Pressurised Water Reactor*. (Hologram made in the Department of Physics at Loughborough University of Technology, England, under the auspices of Holoco Ltd., Shepperton Studio Centre, Middlesex, England, by a team directed by Nick Phillips.)

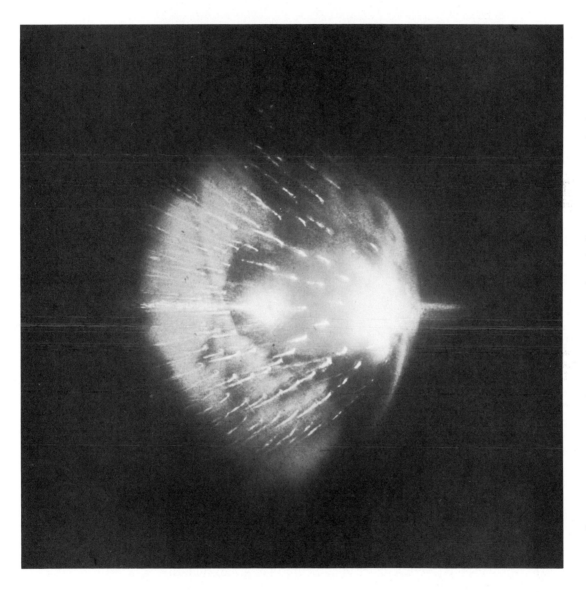

Ruben Nuñez. *Rings of Energy*. 1978. White light transmission hologram (8″ x 10″). Technical assistance: Jody Burns, The New York Art Alliance, Inc. Collection of the artist. (photo Nancy Safford)

Daniel K. Schweitzer. *Time Scape*. 1978. White light
transmission hologram. Scene sculpture: Daniel K.
Schweitzer. Mastering facility: New York Holographic
Labs. Producer: New York Holographic Labs and the
Cabin Creek Center for Work & Environmental
Studies. Collection of the Museum of Holography.
Copyright, Daniel K. Schweitzer, 1978. (photo Nancy
Safford)

Ruben Nuñez. *Venice.* 1978. White light transmission hologram (8″ x 10″).
Technical assistance: Jody Burns, The New York Art Alliance, Inc. Collection
of the Museum of Holography. (photo Sorin Radu)

F.T.S. Yu. *One-Step Rainbow Holograms.* 1978.
(Courtesy F.T.S. Yu, Wayne State University)

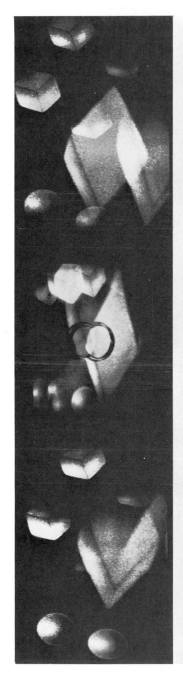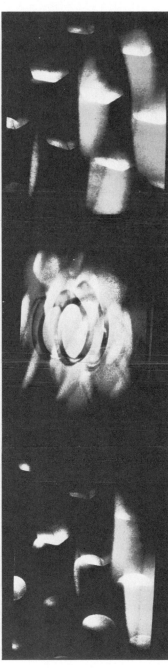

Rudie Berkhout. *Twelve Milliwatt Boogie*. (1978). Artist, systems designer and producer: Rudie Berkhout. Studio: New York Holographic Lab. An almost infinite number of compositions of imagery and color may be observed depending on the viewer's position in relation to the hologram. The left, center and right panels are depicted three times each.

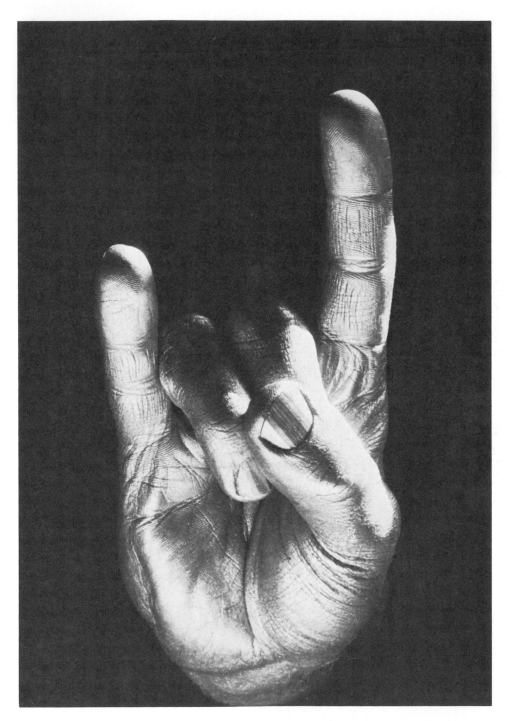

Carl Frederik Reuterswärd. *Finger Language.* 1973. Reflection hologram.
Engineer: Hans Bjelkhagen. Collection of the Museum of Holography.
Copyright, Carl Frederik Reuterswärd, 1973.
(photo: Hans Hammarskiold/Tio)

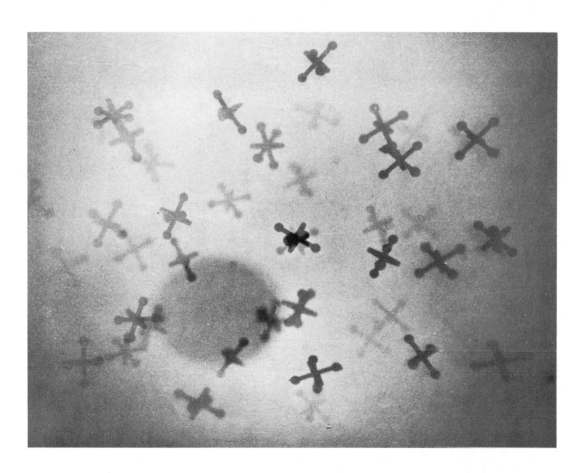

Rick Silberman. *Ball and Jacks*. 1976. Reflection hologram. Collection of the Museum of Holography. Copyright, Rick Silberman, 1976. (photo Brad Cantos)

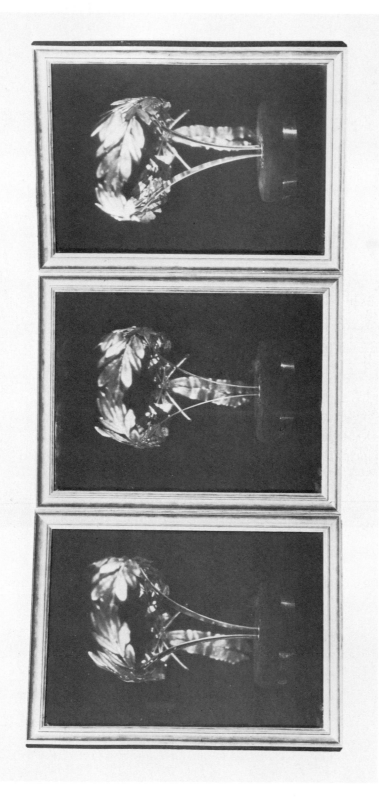

Three views of the "Gold Award" hologram. The gold laurel wreath award (International Award for Valour in Sport) was the object for this white light reflection hologram. An argon ion gas laser was used, and the master hologram plate measured 50 cm by 60 cm. The final hologram was color-tuned by a special technique so that the image produced was as near in color as possible to the Award itself. (Hologram made in the Department of Physics at Loughborough University of Technology, England, under the auspices of Holoco Ltd., Shepperton Studio Centre, Middlesex, England, by a team directed by Nick Phillips.)

Lloyd Cross. *Kiss II*. 1974. 120-degree white light
integral hologram. Collection of the Museum of
Holography. Copyright, Lloyd Cross, 1974. (photo
Daniel E. Quat)

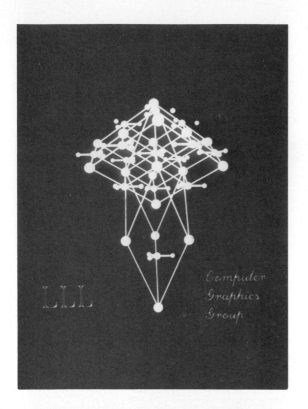
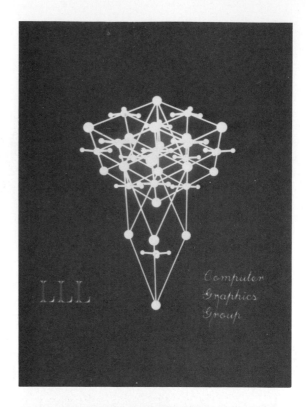

Top: *Calcite*. Bottom: *Tetraglycine*. Produced in cooperation with the Computer Graphics Group of the Lawrence Livermore Laboratory. Each of the rotating multiplex hologram shows the student a 3-dimensional holographic model of a molecule. (Courtesy Multiplex Co.)

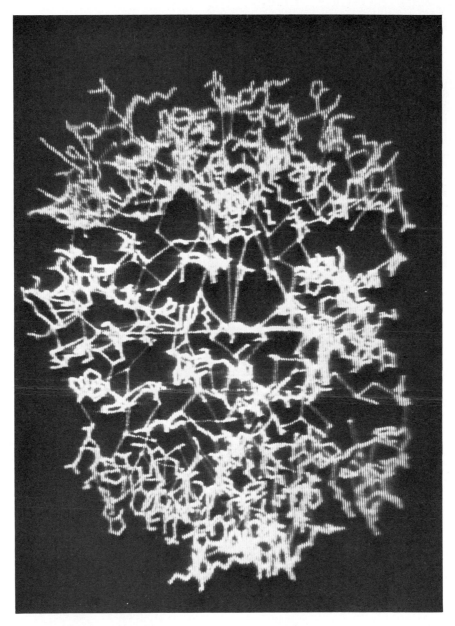

Cyrus Leventhal, Hart Perry, Christos Tountas.
Hemoglobin Molecule. 1974. 360-degree white light
integral hologram. Collection of the Museum of
Holography. Copyright, the artists, 1977. (photo
Daniel E. Quat)

Peter Claudius. *Disco.* Multiplex hologram in
120-degree curved and 360-degree cylindrical format.
Viewable by an ordinary, unfrosted, vertical filament
100-watt bulb. (Courtesy Multiplex Co.)

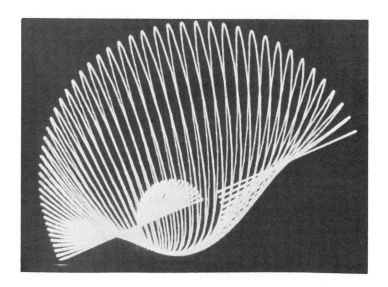

Hart Perry, Jr. and Christos Tountas. *Birth of Venus,*
1977. 360-degree white light integral hologram.
Collection of the Museum of Holography. Copyright,
the artists, 1977. (photo Hart Perry, Jr.)

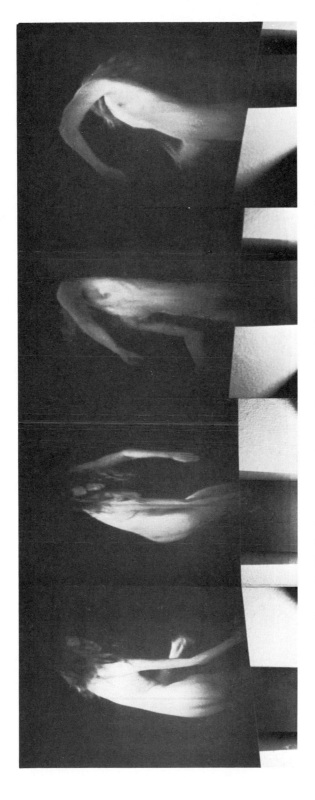

Amy Greenfield. *Saskya.* 1977. A 120-degree multiplex hologram of a dancer. Camera: Hart Perry, Jr. Producer: Cabin Creek Center for Work & Environmental Studies, Artist-In-Residency Program. Processing: Holographic Film Co. Photos by Robert Haller.

Hart Perry. *Marcello Mastrioianni.* 1977. 120-degree
white light integral hologram. (Limited edition)
Facility: The Holographic Film Co. (photo Bill Molteni)

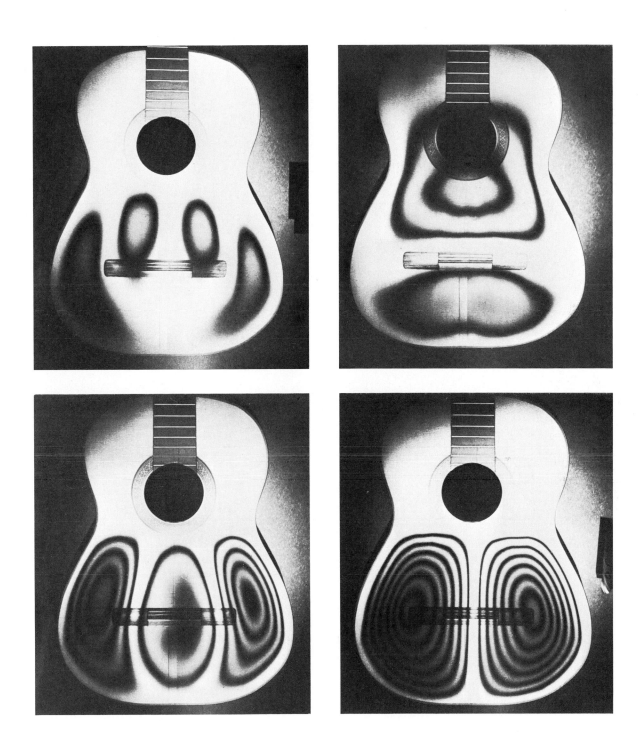

K.A. Stetson and N.E. Molin. *Time-averaged fringes on a clamped guitar* vibrating at different frequencies. These studies were made at the Institute of Optical Research, Stockholm, in 1971. (Courtesy K.A. Stetson, United Technologies Research Center.)

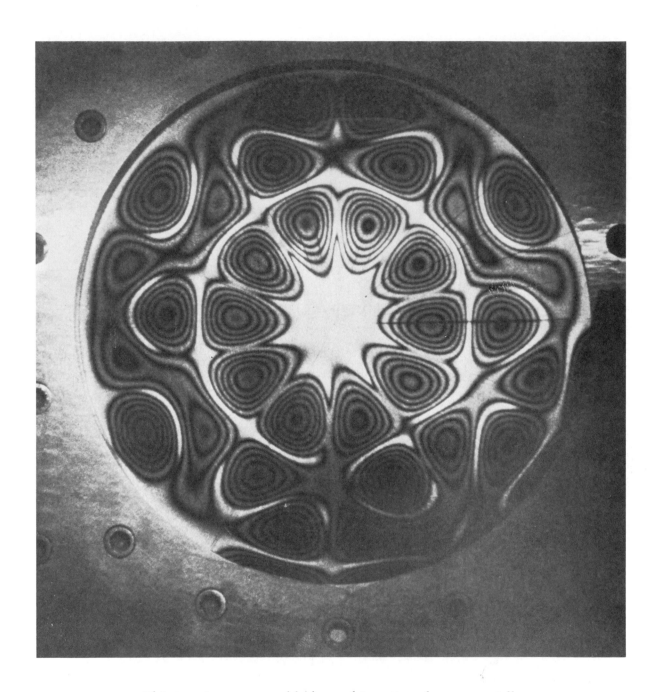

This is a *time-averaged holographic pattern* from a partially clamped ten inch diameter aluminum plate being excited at a resonant frequency of 16,847 Hz by a piezoelectric driver. (Courtesy Gene E. Maddux, Air Force Flight Dynamics Laboratory, Wright-Patterson AFB.)

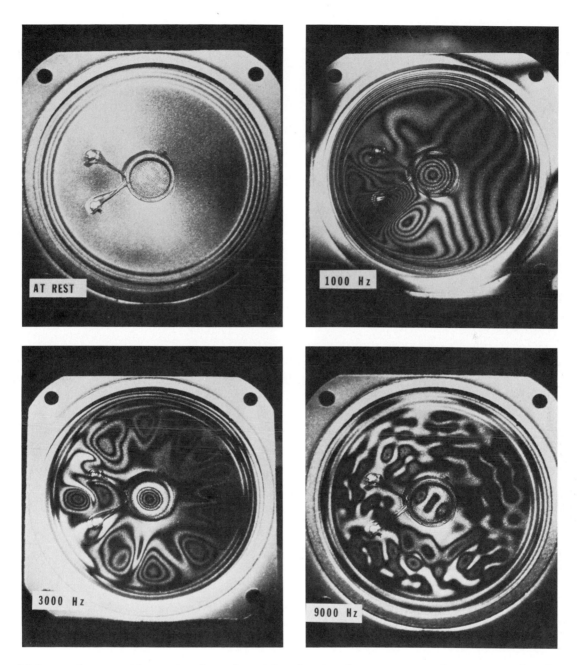

Holography provides a simple and rapid technique for mapping vibration amplitude and mode shapes of objects with opaque, non-optical surfaces. The four photographs show the reconstruction of *time-averaged holographic interferograms*, the result of a radio's speaker being activated by an audio oscillator. In the upper left photo, there was no oscillator output. In the other photos the oscillator was maintained at 1000 Hz, 3000 Hz and 9000 Hz respectively during the exposure of the holograms. A He-Ne laser was used and the exposure time for the holograms was approximately 10 seconds. (Courtesy R.F. Wuerker, TRW Systems Group.)

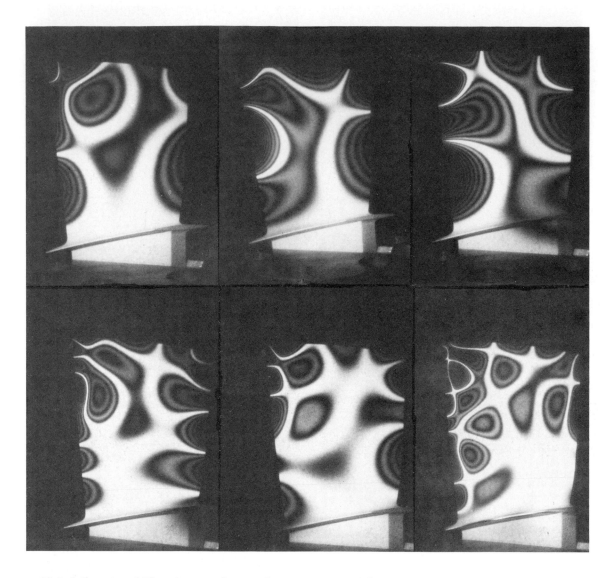

D.J. Monnier, *Vibration analysis of a compressor blade.* Time-averaged holograms. (Courtesy Detroit Diesel Allison, Division of General Motors Corp.)

D.J. Monnier. *4-wheel drive drop box under load* inspected by pulsed holography. 200 microsecond pulse separation. (Courtesy Detroit Diesel Allison, Division of General Motors Corp.)

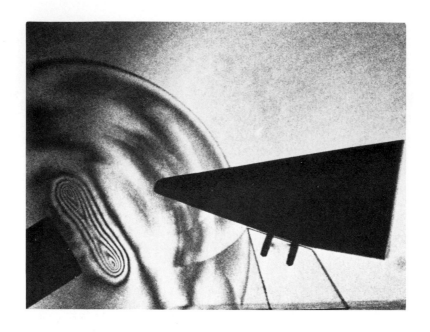

Top: This is a *double-exposure pulsed laser hologram* of a shock wave impinging on a reentry vehicle model.
Bottom: *Time-averaged hologram* of a graphite-epoxy composite plate laced in a support frame to simulate a freely supported plate in bending. The plate was excited by a piezoelectric driver. (Both pictures courtesy Gene E. Maddux, Air Force Flight Dynamics Laboratory, Wright-Patterson AFB.)

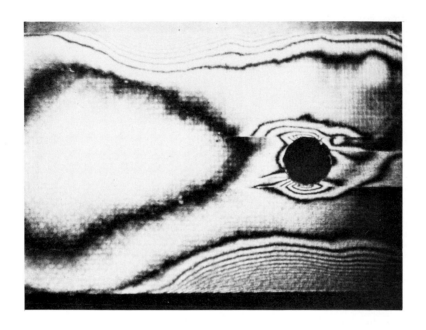

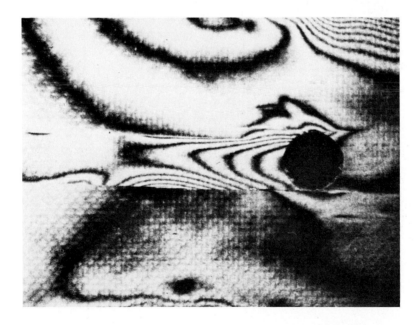

Top & bottom: *Double-exposure holograms* of a graphite-epoxy composite fatigue specimen when a small amount of heating is applied between exposures. Areas of damage due to delamination are indicated around the hole and at the edge of the specimen by the large fringe density. (Photos courtesy Gene E. Maddux, Air Force Flight Dynamics Laboratory, Wright-Patterson AFB.)

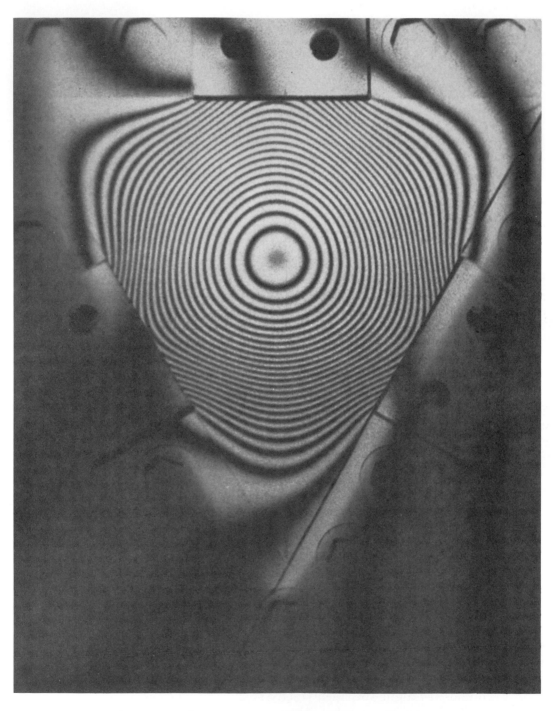

Interferometric fringe pattern obtained from a *double-exposure hologram* wherein a uniform pressure was applied to a partially clamped equilateral triangle between exposures. (Courtesy Gene E. Maddux, Air Force Flight Dynamics Laboratory, Wright-Patterson AFB.)

Holographic interferogram of a collapsing balloon. Taken with an Apollo double-pulse holographic ruby laser. Time interval between pulses 50 microseconds. (Courtesy Ralph Page, Apollo Lasers, Inc.)

Holographic contour map showing a laboratory scene. The
double-exposure hologram was recorded with a pulsed ruby
laser. The frequency (color) of the laser was slightly changed
between the two exposures and resulted in clearly visible contour
fringes. Fringe intervals of one centimeter and greater are
attainable. Note that both interior and exterior surfaces of the
tilted box are contoured. (Courtesy R.F. Wuerker, TRW Systems
Group.)

Photograph of the reconstruction of a *double-exposure hologram* of a light bulb. The light was off for the first exposure and on for the second. The interference fringes result from heating of the gas inside the bulb. (Courtesy R.F. Wuerker, TRW Systems Group.)

Photograph of the reconstruction of a *double-exposure hologram* of a 22-caliber bullet in flight. The hologram, recorded with a pulsed ruby laser, shows the shock wave and interference fringes surrounding the bullet. (Courtesy R.F. Wuerker, TRW Systems Group.)

Photograph of the reconstruction of a *double-exposure hologram* of a 22-caliber bullet and an electric discharge. The hologram was recorded with a pulsed ruby laser. The first exposure recorded the diffuse scene, and the second the scene with its aerodynamic phenomena. The spherical shock wave was created by an electric spark discharge of a capacitor; the other shock wave was caused by the high-speed bullet passing nearby. (Courtesy R.F. Wuerker, TRW Systems Group.)

BIBLIOGRAPHY

BOOKS

Beesley, M.J., *Lasers and Their Applications (2nd ed.)*, Halsted Press (Div. John Wiley), New York, 1976

Benthall, J., *Science and Technology in Art*, Praeger, New York, 1972

Brecht, G., *Chance-Imagery*, Something Else Press, New York, 1966

Brett, G., *Kinetic Art: The Language of Movement*, Van Nostrand-Reinhold, New York, 1968

Cathey, W.T., *Optical Information Processing and Holography*, Wiley-Interscience, New York, 1974

Caulfield, H.J. and Lu, S., *The Applications of Holography*, Wiley-Interscience, New York, 1970.

Collier, R.J., Burckhardt, C.J., and Lin, L.H., *Optical Holography*, Academic Press, New York, 1971

Cox, A., *Photographic Optics*, Focal Press, London, 1966

Davis, D., *Art and the Future*, Praeger, New York, 1973

DeVelis, J.B., and Reynolds, G.O., *Theory and Applications of Holography*, Addison-Wesley, Reading, Mass., 1967

Ditchburn, R.W., *Light (3rd ed.)*, Academic Press, New York, 1976

Dowbenko, G., *Homegrown Holography (2nd ed.)*, Amphoto, Garden City, New York, 1978

Francon, M., *Holography*, Academic Press, New York, 1974

Gillon, E.V. Jr., (Ed.), *Geometric Design and Ornament*, Dover Publications, New York, 1969

Goldman, L., *Applications of the Laser*, CRC Press, Cleveland, 1973

Hornung, C.P., *Handbook of Designs and Devices*, Dover Publications, New York, 1959

Jenkins, F.A., and White, H.E., *Fundamentals of Optics*, McGraw-Hill, New York, 1976

Jeong, T.H., *A Study Guide on Holography*, Lake Forest College, Illinois, 1975

Kallard, T., *Exploring Laser Light*, Optosonic Press, New York, 1977

Kock, W.E., *Lasers and Holography*, Doubleday/Anchor, Garden City, NY 1969

Kepes, G., *The Language of Vision*, Paul Theobald, Chicago, 1944

Larcher, J., *Geometrical Designs & Optical Art*, Dover Publications, New York, 1974

Lehmann, M., *Holography — Technique and Practice*, Focal Press, London, and Hastings House, New York, 1970

Lipson, H., (Ed.), *Optical Transforms*, Academic Press, New York, 1972

Malina, F., (Ed.), *Kinetic Art: Theory and Practice*, Dover Publications, New York, 1974

McLuhan, M., *Understanding Media: The Extensions of Man*, McGraw-Hill, New York, 1964

Meyer-Arendt, J.R., *Introduction to Classical and Modern Optics*, Prentice-Hall, Englewood Cliffs, 1972

Moholy-Nagy, L., *Vision in Motion*, Paul Theobald, Chicago, 1947

Moholy-Nagy, S., *Moholy-Nagy: Experiment in Totality (2nd ed.)*, MIT Press, Cambridge, Mass., 1969

Neblette, C.B. (Ed.), *Photography: Its Materials and Processes (7th ed.)*, Van Nostrand, Princeton, 1976

Okoshi, T., *Three-Dimensional Imaging Techniques*, Academic Press, New York, 1976

Ouchi, H., *Japanese Optical and Geometrical Art*, Dover Publications, New York, 1977

Outwater, C., and Van Hammersweld, E., *A Guide to Practical Holography*, Pentangle Press, Beverly Hills, California, 1974

Parola, R., *Optical Art*, Reinhold, New York, 1969

Reutersvärd, C.F., *Laser*, Wahlstrom, Stockholm, 1969

Schawlow, A. (Ed.), *Lasers and Light: Reprints from Scientific American*, W.E. Freeman, San Francisco, Calif., 1969

Schenk, S.M. (Ed.), *Who's Who in Display Holography*, Museum of Holography, New York, 1978

Smith, H.M., *Principles of Holography (2nd ed.)*, Wiley, New York, 1975

Stroke, G.W., *Introduction to Coherent Optics and Holography (2nd ed.)*, Academic Press, New York, 1969

Van Heel, A.C.S., and Velzel, C.H.F., *What Is Light*, McGraw-Hill, New York, 1968

Wall, F.J., and Jordan, F.I., *Photographic Facts and Formulas*, Amphoto, Garden City, New York, 1974

Yu, F.T.S., *Introduction to Diffraction, Information Processing and Holography*, MIT Press, Cambridge, Mass., 1973

Catalogues

Holografi: Det 3-Dimensionella Mediet. House of Culture, Stockholm, Sweden (March 12-28, 1976).

Through the Looking Glass, the Opening Exhibition of the Museum of Holography (December 8, 1976 – February 27, 1977). Museum of Holography, 1976

Furst, A., Phillips, N., and Wolff, J., (Holoco Ltd.), *Light Fantastic*, at the Royal Academy of Arts, London (March, 1977). Bergstrom & Boyle Books, London, 1977

Harriet Casdin-Silver: Holography, Museum of Holography, (May 4 – July 24, 1977)

Holograms by Holoco: *Light Fantastic II*, Presented by Guinness at the Royal Academy of Arts, London (January 12 – March 27, 1978), Bergstrom & Boyle Books, London, 1978

Carl Frederik Reutersvärd: 25 Years in the Branch. Museum of Holography (September 7 – November 27, 1978)

Holokinetics: Ruben Nuñez. Museum of Holography (September 7 – November 27, 1978)

Journals

Architectural Forum,   *Art and Architecture,*   *Art in America,*

Art International,   *Art Journal,*   *Art News,*   *Arts Magazine,*

Artforum,   *holosphere,*   *Laser Focus,*   *Laser + Elektro-Optik,*

Leonardo,   *Optical Spectra,*   *Radical Software,*   *Studio International,*

Techne.